Dedication

This book is dedicated to the memory of Ennis William Cosby, whose special gift was to provide a unique learning environment for everyone he met. "Hello Friend" was his typical greeting. By discovering and understanding his learning difference, he was able to develop many unique opportunities for others. Meeting Ennis compelled me to transform my dreams into action and carry on his vision of honoring our differences.

ACKNOWLEDGMENTS

Many thanks goes to all the children and parents who have struggled to find hope and peace! You have made me aware of the need for fun, tasty, creative foods to help bring stability to an erratic digestive system.

Profound thanks to Dr. Camille Cosby. Her encouragement gave me the fortitude to pursue this vision when it seemed insurmountable. Her integrity and commitment to excellence has given me the inspiration to pursue my goal of providing an environment of hope to all children. She has helped me remain focused and committed to my dreams.

Likewise to Dr. Bill Cosby. His genius and continued support to help me stay focused on educating the whole person has been a great inspiration. He has given me so many wonderful ideas to express, simply, a very complicated concept of changing diet. His commitment to education is matched only by that of his wife.

Thanks to Dr. Barry Sears, whose research has given us a way to prepare a physiologically sound meal. His availability to consult with me has always been appreciated. His research helped me understand why so many children have neurological problems.

Thanks to Dr. Daniel Amen, I now understand those with learning differences, such as ADD, ADHD, dyslexia and depression. His research with SPECT analysis gives us a very important diagnostic tool to understand why different brains respond differently to the same stimulus.

Many thanks to Dr. Bruce Holub, who has always been available to answer questions regarding fatty acid research and food composition. His extensive published research has set the foundation for understanding why fatty acids are so essential to life.

Also to Nutrasource Diagnostics, Inc. who give us the ability to determine the fatty acid composition of the blood and therefore determine why a patient's neurology is in trouble. We now have a reliable way to recommend fatty acid supplementation.

Thanks to Dr. Julie Conquer of Ontario, Canada. Because of her efforts, we have a better understanding of fatty acid analysis and a way to measure neurological impairment.

Thanks to Jennifer Smith for bringing my creative ideas into reality. Her artistic ability and creative layout ideas helped make this a fun and informative book.

Thanks to Penney Hoffman, Jeff Woodward, Michael Dixon, and Ann Bonthuis, the chefs who helped make these delicious recipes that are so easy to prepare.

Special thanks to the parents and children in the Bronx who tested the recipes and helped me determine what would be fun and easy for families.

Thanks to Claudia Murray, whose photography highlights these delicious recipes.

A very special thanks to my niece, Christa Bonthuis, who helped me refine and edit the manuscript. Her dedication is greatly appreciated.

Thanks to Jay Donahue for his editing expertise. What a difference he made!.

POWERFUL FOOD FOR POWERFUL MINDS & BODIES

A Family Handbook

by René Thomas, D.C., N.D.

With Nature's Mighty Bites™

Hampton University Press
Hampton University
Hampton, Virginia 23668

Visit the Nature's Mighty Bites™ web site: **www.kidsneedusnow.org**
Designed by Jennifer Smith

Library of Congress Cataloging-in-Publication Data

Thomas, René. 1944-
    Powerful Foods For Powerful Minds and Bodies/René Thomas, D.C., N.D.—1st ed.
    p. cm
    Includes bibliographical references and index.
    ISBN 1-932788-02-6
    1. ADD, ADHD, OCD, ODD, Dyslexia—Learning Differences 2. Omega-3 Fatty Acids—EPA/DHA 3. Fish Oil 4. Fatty Acid Analysis 5. Science of Balanced Eating 6. Glycemic Index/Glycemic Load 7. Truth about Food Labels
    I. Title

First Edition: June 2004

10 9 8 7 6 5 4 3 2 1

The Adventures of Nature's Mighty Bites

TABLE OF CONTENTS

Dedication. 3
Acknowledgments 4
Introduction. 7
Foreword 9
Why This Book? 10
Symbols Throughout. 16
Keys To Healthy Eating 17
The Story of Nature's Mighty Bites . . 18
How To Use This Book 27
Let's Get Started 22
Basic Rules of Cooking. 23
General Cooking Tools 24
How Healthy is Our Food 25
How To Read A Label! 26
How To Use This Book 27
Food Charts. 28
Protein Chart 28
Carbohydrate Chart 30
Fat Chart 33
Food Is Our Friend! 34
Would you ever guess.... 39

Breakfast 40

Is This Your Breakfast??? 44
Eggs & Fruit Breakfast. 46
Herb And Fruit Omelet 48
Yogurt & Fruit 50
Mighty Melon 51
Protein Powered Oatmeal 52
Fruit Salad 54
Nut Butter & Apples 55
French Toast 56
Power Pancakes. 58
Mighty Nice Waffles 60
Mighty Nice Toppings 62

Shakes 63

Nut Milk 65
Peachy Cream Shake 66
Peanutty Shake 67
Raspberry Shake 68
Berry Banana Shake 69
Sunshine Shake 70
Blueberry Shake 71
Berry Lime Shake. 72
Creamy Orange Shake 73
Tropical Shake 74
Very Berry Shake. 75
Very Cherry Shake 76
Strawberry Kiwi Shake. 77

Lunch 78

Satay Sauce 79
Salad On The Side 80
Crunchy Almond Roll Up 81
Chicken Kebobs. 82
Power Pizza Crust 84
Power Pizza. 86
Scrambled Egg Boats. 88
Turkey Melt Boats 90
Fluffy Cheese Potato Boats 92
Turkey Log & Fruit Salad 94
Apple Muffin Melt 96
Broccoli Bacon Salad 98
Summer Chicken Salad. 100
Hawaiian Chicken Salad 102
Creamy Potato Soup 104
Tacos 106
Chili 108
Mighty Nice Potato Cakes 110
"Typical American Meal??!!". 113

Did You Know?. 114
Rice And Beans—Perfect Protein??? . 115

Dinner 116

Mighty Tasty Marinade 117
Mandarin Marinade Steak 118
Glazed Chicken 120
Lemon Salmon Steak 122
Spicy Orange Salad 124
Mighty Mac & Cheese 126
Zucchini Chips 128
Salmon Saucers 130
Egg Salad Saucers 132
Tropical Chicken 134
Mighty Nutty Chicken 136
Mighty Nutty Fish Sticks 138
Coconut Crunch Chicken. 140
Coconut Crunch Shrimp 142
Chicken & Corn Fritters 144
BBQ Kebobs. 146
Mighty Nice Tofu Stir Fry. 148
Spaghetti And Meatballs. 150
Meatloaf 152
What Are You Eating? 154

Snacks. 155

High Power Nut Butter 156
Mighty Yummy Cocoa 157
Melon & Protein 158
Spicy Corn Muffin Melt 159
Turkey & Cheese 160
Treat. 160
Crunchy Almond Snack 161
Nutty Banana Snack 162
Mighty Nice Deviled Eggs 163
Cheese & Fruit 164

Cottage Cheese And Fruit 165
Turkey Log And Apple 166
Melted Cheese And Cracker 167
Mighty Nice Nachos 168
Toasted Cheese Panwich. 169
Snacks—What Are You Eating? . . . 170
Would You Ever Guess.... 173

Weekend Treats . . .174

Mighty Nutty Pie Crusts 175
Almond Crust. 175
Brazil Nut Crust 175
Applesauce Muffins. 176
Crispy Potato Skins. 178
Almond Cookies 179
Corn Muffins 180
Chocolate Pudding 182
Fruit Frogurt 184
Mighty Oatmeal Macaroons 186
Chocolate Cookies 188
Cinnasauce Yogurt 189
Blueberry Custard 190
Mighty Sweet Potato Pie. 192
Peach Cobbler. 194
Fruity Gello Snack 196
Weekend—What Are You Eating? . . 198
Glossary. 200
References. 204
Web Sites 204
Publications 204
Food Recommendations 207

Introduction

Our future lies with our children. But based on the epidemic increases in obesity and attention deficit disorders, that future may seem bleak. The growing incidences of adult-onset diabetes in teenagers and the increase in anxiety and depression in all children are additional indicators that something is wrong. Although there are many potential suspects, the primary cause may well be the food we eat.

Food controls our hormones, and hormones ultimately control our lives. It is clear that the hormones that govern our children's lives are careening out of control. But don't despair; if you follow the guidelines in this book, you can be back on the right track to a focused, happier, and healthier life within a matter of weeks.

Eating balanced meals is the key to good health.

Dr. René is one of the early adherents to the Zone principles and its impact on health and behavior—especially in children. This book encapsulates her years of research to understand what it takes to make children want to change their future. But this book is as much for the parents as it is for the children. For if the parents are not part of the solution, then they become the cause of the problem.

I urge you to not only read this book, but also to practice its dietary principles on a lifetime basis. The end result will be a better future for your children, and a better life for all of us.

Dr. Barry Sears

Dr. Sears, the author of The Zone, *was a researcher at Boston University and MIT before forming his own biotechnology company. He started his research, which led to the development of the Zone Diet, to avoid the heart disease that all the males on his father's side of the family developed.*

The Zone *became a number-one* New York Times *best-seller and changed the carbohydrate dominated diet into a balance of protein, carbohydrate and fat. This revolutionized nutritional thinking. His other books include:* Mastering the Zone, Zone Perfect Meals in Minutes, Zone Food Blocks, The Anti-Aging Zone, The Soy Zone *and* The Omega Zone.

OMEGA-3 PROFILE TEST REFERENCES

SELECTED REFERENCES:

- AHA DIETARY GUIDELINES: REVISION 2000: A STATEMENT FOR HEALTHCARE PROFESSIONALS FROM THE NUTRITION COMMITTEE OF THE AMERICAN HEART ASSOCIATION. *CIRCULATION* 102:2284-2299 (2000).

- BUCHER ET AL., N-3 POLYUNSATURATED FATTY ACIDS IN CORONARY HEART DISEASE: A METAANALYSIS OF RANDOMIZED CONTROLLED TRIALS. *AM. J. MED.* 112:298-304 (2002).

- DEWAILLY ET AL., N-3 FATTY ACIDS AND CARDIOVASCULAR DISEASE RISK FACTORS AMONG THE INUIT OF NUNAVIK. *AM. J. CLIN. NUTR.* 74:464-473 (2001).

- ERKKILA ET AL., N-3 FATTY ACIDS AND 5-Y RISKS OF DEATH AND CARDIOVASCULAR DISEASE EVENTS IN PATIENTS WITH CORONARY ARTERY DISEASE. *AM. J. CLIN. NUTR.* 78:65-71(2003).

- GISSI-PREVENZIONE INVESTIGATORS, DIETARY SUPPLEMENTATION WITH N-3 POLYUNSATURATED FATTY ACIDS AND VITAMIN E AFTER MYOCARDIAL INFARCTION: RESULTS OF THE GISSI-PREVENZIONE TRIAL. *LANCET* 354:447-455 (1999).

- HARPER ET AL., THE ROLE OF OMEGA-3 FATTY ACIDS IN THE PREVENTION OF CORONARY HEART DISEASE. *ARCH. INT. MED.* 161:2185-2192 (2001).

- HJARTAKER ET AL., SERUM PHOSPHOLIPID FATTY ACID COMPOSITION AND HABITUAL INTAKE OF MARINE FOODS REGISTERED BY A SEMI-QUANTITITIVE FOOD FREQUENCY QUESTIONNAIRE. *EUR. J. CLIN. NUTR.* 51:736-742 (1997).

- HOLUB B., CLINICAL NUTRITION:4. OMEGA-3 FATTY ACIDS IN CARDIOVASCULAR CARE. CMAJ 166(5):608-615 (2002).

- KRIS-ETHERTON ET AL., OMEGA-3 FATTY ACIDS AND CARDIOVASCULAR DISEASE: NEW RECOMMENDATIONS FROM THE AMERICAN HEART ASSOCIATION. *ARTERIOSCLER. THROMB VASC BIOL.* 23:151-152 (2003).

- KOBAYASHI ET AL., SINGLE MEASUREMENT OF SERUM PHOSPHOLIPID FATTY ACID AS A BIOMARKER OF SPECIFIC FATTY ACID INTAKE IN MIDDLE-AGED JAPANESE MEN. *EUR. J. CLIN. NUTR.* 55:643-650 (2001).

- LEMAITRE ET AL., N-3 POLYUNSATURATED FATTY ACIDS, FATAL ISCHEMIC HEART DISEASE, AND NONFATAL MYOCARDIAL INFARCTION IN OLDER ADULTS: THE CARDIOVASCULAR HEALTH STUDY. *AM. J. CLIN. NUTR.* 77:319-325 (2003).

- O'KEEFE ET AL., FROM INUIT TO IMPLEMENTATION: OMEGA-3 FATTY ACIDS COME OF AGE. MAYO CLIN. PROC. 75:607-614 (2000).

- RISSANEN ET AL., FISH-OIL DERIVED FATTY ACIDS, DOCOSAHEXAENOIC ACID AND DOCOSAPENTAENOIC ACID, AND THE RISK OF ACUTE CORONARY EVENTS: THE KUOPIO ISCHAEMIC HEART DISEASE RISK FACTOR STUDY. *CIRCULATION* 102:2677-2679 (2000).

- SCHMIDT ET AL., N-3 FATTY ACIDS FROM FISH AND CORONARY ARTERY DISEASE: IMPLICATIONS FOR PUBLIC HEALTH. *PUBLIC HEALTH NUTR.* 31:91-98 (2000).

- SIMON ET AL., SERUM FATTY ACIDS AND THE RISK OF CORONARY HEART DISEASE. *AM. J. EPIDEMIOL.* 142:469-476 (1995).

- SIMOPOULOS ET AL., ESSENTIALITY OF AND RECOMMENDED DIETARY INTAKES FOR OMEGA-6 AND OMEGA-3 FATTY ACIDS. *ANN. NUTR. METAB.* 43:127-130 (1999).

FOREWORD

Powerful Foods for Powerful Minds & Bodies featuring Nature's Mighty Bites™, by René Thomas, D.C., N.D., is a bellwether to re-strengthen and substantiate an old adage, "You are what you eat."

To eat, drink, and then be truthfully merry for more than an hour requires some major changes in what many of us regularly consume. Unequivocally, those changes will not occur until we want them to. But one must be aware of the possibilities before one can address the want.

The possibilities relating to food, as shown in this book, will not make us feel deprived of the usual unhealthy goodies. Instead, we will feel emotionally and physically balanced.

The general media have informed the public about the ballooning rates of diabetes and obesity amongst adults and children in the United States of America. Additionally, there have been considerable reports about parents' woes due to their children's hyperactivity, lethargy, and learning differences. Hopefully, very soon, physicians, social scientists and educators will focus on healthful foods to help eradicate the aforementioned problems before so eagerly prescribing or suggesting medications for adults and, particularly, for our children.

Some schools have taken big action steps to eliminate junk foods such as sodas, candies, and cupcakes. For example, Los Angeles Unified and Capistrano Unified school districts in California have already moved to ban many junk foods and carbonated drinks. Hopefully, others will join with them to offer young people healthy foods and drinks to combat potential ill health.

The elimination of junk foods will also increase mental clarity. Far too many young people's minds are muddled because of bad nutrition. The chips and sodas many students subsist on do not provide adequate brain fuel.

Social scientists and advertisers know that repetitive images and messages influence our perceptions, thinking, and desires. Food scientists know that sugar, salt, unhealthy fats, and most refined carbohydrates stimulate our sense of taste and, therefore, our appetites.

So, be knowledgeable about food, and eat, drink, be merry and feel good all day, each day. Enjoy the recipes in this superb, informative book.

Camille O. Cosby, Ed.D.
January 2003

WHY THIS BOOK?

For the last 22 years, I have been treating patients, teaching seminars, and doing clinical research dealing with children and adults with learning differences. In the early '80s helping those with specific learning problems was relatively simple. By changing the diet, with the addition of visual therapy and neurological re-education, a very high percentage of children and adults responded quickly with excellent results. Starting in 1985, as low-fat, high-carbohydrate diets became popular, the same therapies did not work as fast. Because the results took so long, many in the treatment program dropped out. Those who participated saw some results, but with peer pressure and school stresses, it was becoming more and more obvious that many turned to prescription drugs to solve the behavior, concentration, and learning problems. Do prescription drugs solve the problem? Not really, however, many school systems are demanding that prescription drugs be used to control behavior problems.

DRUG USE AMONG CHILDREN

Prescription drug use among even kindergarten children has risen to unbelievable proportions. Most of the children do not like the feelings they have while taking the drugs. They lose their appetites, have robotic behavior and become lethargic. Studies have shown that a high percentage of those who have been on Ritalin or Adderall in childhood turn to cocaine or other street drugs as they get older. If the numbers continue to rise, we will have a drug-ridden youth population who may become major drug users in adulthood. Is there another approach that can be taken? Is there a reason for the rising behavioral problems and learning difficulties?

DIETARY CHANGES

In 1996 the explanation became apparent—high insulin blood values and excessively low fatty acid profiles. Further research showed that in 1985 the high carbohydrate, low fat, no fat diet became prevalent. At this time, complex carbohydrate use rose 115%, obesity rose 32% and essential fat intake decreased by 14%. These are very significant statistics—complex carbohydrate use causes insulin to rise, which leads to obesity and inhibition of the essential fatty acids. In an age where the word "fat" is considered a "bad" three-letter word, new research has shown that these essential fatty acids are crucial for life—without them the hormonal system becomes inefficient, the communication network of the body slows down, and, in some instances, becomes dormant.

With this information I began a new approach—teaching parents and children how to eat a balanced diet of the foods they like with the addition of the essential fatty acids in supplement form. Dr. Barry Sears made a huge impact in the field of biochemistry of food by showing that there is a physiological and biochemical formula that the brain and body require to work efficiently. In 1998 a blood test became available to measure the fatty acid profile of the body. The results were astounding—100% of the patients I tested showed severe fatty acid deficiencies.

MEASURABLE WAYS TO DETERMINE THE PROBLEM

Knowing how important the fatty acid analysis was to understanding a patient's health, it became imperative to find a laboratory whose quality control was impeccable. I was introduced to Dr. Bruce Holub of the University of Guelph, in Guelph, Ontario, Canada. He is the world's expert in EPA, the most important fatty acid, and a wonderful consultant regarding fatty acids and food composition. He introduced me to Nutrasource Diagnostics, Inc., the number one lab in North America for fatty acid analysis.

In 1998 I was introduced to Dr. Daniel Amen of Fairfield and Newport Beach, California. He is doing SPECT analysis of the brain and giving a visual explanation of brain function and dysfunction. With his databank of more than 19,000 scans, we have a visual image of the brain and are able to understand the different types of Attention Deficit Disorder (ADD), Attention Deficit Hyperactivity Disorder (ADHD), Obsessive Compulsive Disorder (OCD), Oppositional Defiant Disorder (ODD), dyslexia and depression.

I was elated! We now had a blood test, a brain scan that showed brain, blood flow, a diet and supplementation that could make the necessary changes along with a way to measure that we did what we said we did! The answer now seemed easy—change the diet to a balance of protein, carbohydrate, and fat, add the essential fatty acids and the problem was solved! What a breakthrough!

EASY? NO WAY!

Not so easy. The parents and children were excited about the prospects of the discovery but World War 30 occurred—change their food plan! Take fish oil!

My frustration was that the answer seemed so easy, yet it was difficult to help the parents and children understand that the dietary changes were not restrictions or punishments, but rather a choice for a better lifestyle plan that would solve so many problems they were having in their everyday lives.

Instead of looking for the answers in a textbook, I decided to ask the parents and children what they needed. I went to the homes and talked with the families, I gave lectures to family groups, I conducted small clinical studies and then finally larger studies in different areas of the country. What I found was astounding—there was so much confusion about diet that resistance to change was at a heightened level. The other astounding fact was that very few families sat together around a table to eat a meal. Each family member's schedule was so hectic that many times meals were frozen dinners, cold cereal or fast food. Children were filling up on fast-food carbohydrates, so much so that even if there was a family meal they had no appetite and ate very little.

THE PLAN

I soon realized that I had to come up with a plan to teach families how to eat the food they liked in a balanced and tasty manner. It had to be fun, creative, and catchy so they would be excited about the prospect and willing to try a new approach. Realizing that balanced food was imperative, I began to research a way to make the foods that children liked with healthier ingredients but with the same flavors that they craved. I needed to find a way to enrich the food with the essential fatty acids. Those who participated in the clinical studies, and followed the program, had great results in a short period of time. Dyslexia was alleviated, ADD, ADHD, and depression became nonexistent. I gave brochures to the families and those who enjoyed cooking found the changes easy to follow. People who had trouble cooking new and creative meals dropped out. Some were willing to work with the children to take the liquid EPA/DHA and others, due to their own personal problem with fish oil, refused to give it to their children even if the children were willing to take it. The answers were easy but compliance was difficult for many. School administrators saw the need but neglected the responsibility.

From this experience I realized I needed to provide simple easy ways to help them make the changes—tasty recipes, illustrated and colorful directions and an essential fatty acid supplement. This led to the production of the cookbook and a microencapsulated EPA/DHA supplement, Nature's Mighty 3s™, that can be added to all the recipes and has no flavor or odor, if used as directed in the recipes.

The next step was to have children test the recipes. I chose those who used the program to be the Board of Directors. In the testing stage of the book, I found that adults liked the recipes along with the children. Reports are that the food is fun, tasty, and easy to make. Some families have now started to sit down at the table and eat together, and many of the children like to help their parents prepare meals. Mealtime can be a very important time of the day for families to come together, to share a meal and their experiences of the day. **Hopefully this book will help mealtime become a family affair!**

THE ANSWER

Food and essential fatty acids may not be the entire solution for the severe learning difficulties so many are experiencing, but they lay the groundwork and the foundation on which to build a neurological and hormonal system that has the essential tools needed to live a productive life. The next steps involve the teachers and counselors who understand each child's difference and ability, to help the children become all they can be.

THE TEST

I have been measuring fatty acids levels in the blood since 1998. Thanks to the research at the University of Guelph, in Guelph, Ontario, we now have parameters to understand a great deal about fatty acid levels in the blood. Because of the research by Dr. Julie Conquer, we have a way to measure indications of cognitive impairment, dementia, and Alzheimer tendencies. Thanks to the research of Dr. Bruce Holub we have parameters to measure cardiovascular risk and immune system strength. It is always exciting to be able to measure health risks so something can be done before problems become irreversible. A simple blood test, available within the United States, through your physician, or have it done yourself through Your Future Health (see page 202), gives us the information we need to take charge of our lives. The values that are the most important in the blood test are:

• **Arachidonic acid (AA) to Eicosapentaenoic Acid (EPA) ratio**—Too much arachidonic acid can become a hormonal nightmare. It is a major cause of inflammation in the body. It interferes with EPA's ability to increase blood flow throughout the body.

- **Omega-6 to Omega-3 Ratio**—Both Omega-3 and Omega-6 fatty acids are necessary in our diet. However, the typical American diet is very plentiful in the Omega-6 fatty acids and extremely deficient in the Omega-3 fatty acids. It is important to have a one-to-one ratio of Omega-6 to Omega-3 fatty acids.

  Omega-6 fatty acids include vegetable oils such as sunflower, safflower, corn, cottonseed and soybeans oils, and plant oils such as evening primrose, black currant seed and borage.

  Omega-3 fatty acids are found in deep-sea fish and flax seed oil. Fish oil is the most efficient form of EPA/DHA.

- **EPA—Eicosapentaenoic Acid**—The most important of the long chain Omega-3 fatty acids which help prevent inflammation. It increases both dopamine and serotonin and helps decrease high levels of cortisol. It activates all the hormones.

- **DHA**—A critical fatty acid for brain function. It is important for cell membranes to be able to transfer information and for the retina to receive visual input.

- **Threshold Level**—This tells us how well we are dampening arachidonic acid. The lower the value, the better.

- **EPA+DHA**—The higher the value, the greater protection we have to prevent ischemic heart disease.

THE CONCERN

The excitement of having a test to measure fatty acid levels was soon overshadowed by the startling results. How could so many people have cardiovascular problems, and diabetic and Alzheimer's tendencies? The scary part is that the numbers were so severe and not limited to adults. Children had blood values so pathological that it became clear we will have a very serious problem if we do not make changes quickly.

NORMAL					
AA/EPA	N6/N3	EPA	DHA	Threshold	EPA+DHA
3	1	7	6	0.2-0.5	8.5
MEAN RESULTS					
AA/EPA	N6/N3	EPA	DHA	Threshold	EPA+DHA
25	7	0.25	2	55	2.25

These results are not from one or two tests, but hundreds of tests done since 1998. What is of great concern is that the results are worse each time I take new samples! When I did the last group, many of the parents cried when they saw their results. They thought they were providing healthy meals for their children yet the blood tells the truth. The food we think is healthy is contributing to the demise of our children's health and well-being. No wonder so many are diagnosed with ADD, ADHD, OCD, depression, and dyslexia!

WHAT CAN BE DONE?

When the parents got over the shock, we had a food-tasting party. As we were setting up for the party, the children and the parents were very restless. Once they ate, everyone calmed down. They didn't feel sleepy; they were focused and had energy to do the day's activities. They ate less than normal and enjoyed the food more. They were surprised how their appetites were satisfied with balanced foods. I have been doing these demonstrations for the past five years and the results are always the same. **Crappy eating leads to stinking thinking and broken bodies. Healthy eating leads to creative thinking and, therefore, strong bodies!**

THE REAL CHALLENGE

We have become a society of pills, potions and high carbohydrates. Television pushes fast food meals, and billboards entice children to get a toy along with a happy meal. We complain about the problem it presents, we blame children for their behavior, we are horrified at the violence, and the press reports that those who do the violence are getting younger and younger! Parents are blamed for the child's behavior, yet the media bombards children to choose sugar laden, trans fat fast meals. It is time we take a stand to educate parents and children that life style commitment is the ultimate solution.

The challenge is to help individuals understand that how we eat is the most important factor in maintaining a healthy body and mind. We make sure our cars are filled with fuel so they run properly. When we go on a long trip we check the oil and fill the gas tank. We watch the gas indicator to make sure we fill the tank periodically. Yet we skip meals, eat junk, and then get angry when our body sputters and we get sick. Very few have studied the basic principles of food science, and even if taught, tend to ignore the simple rules of eating, for it takes time to prepare the proper food and to find the ingredients to cook the food. Food can be an emotional issue—we sedate ourselves with meals full of carbohydrates, saturated and trans fats and take pills to hide the pain. It is painful to watch adults who know better ignore a child's need for healthy food because of so-called time constraints. The one who provides food for the family is the one who can help the family choose health or contribute to the environment of a disease-ridden society. The most difficult to watch is a school system that provides foods loaded with sugars and trans fats in order to make money at the expense of the beautiful minds and then complain about the behavior problems that are the result.

A headline in the *Tucson Citizen* on September 22, 2003 states that "Firms spend billions to push junk food on schools." The article goes on to say that billions of dollars are used to influence food choices for children, as fast food restaurants sponsor fund-raisers and provide marketing material that promotes snacks. Some Board of Education groups want to banish junk food, yet critics claim that obesity would not be solved by banning junk food and many schools rely heavily on snack sales and fundraisers for extra money. Money at the expense of our children! KIDS NEED US NOW! Are we up to the challenge, or is money a motivation to maintain the status quo!

Many have tried to tell me that children will not eat healthy food—my experience says differently. The majority will eat, healthy, tasty, colorful food if it's prepared in a fun way. Some are so addicted to junk that you must first balance their junk food until they are able to make healthier choices. I observed this while working with a school in the Bronx. The children wanted healthy food, they craved it, they ate all the food and wanted to share with others. It was obvious they were hungry—they had the courage to write letters to the principal asking for better food—a brave thing for 3rd and 4th graders. The administration smiled when they read the letter and then filed it away out of sight so as not to have a reminder that the children really want healthy things to eat. The food program was stopped because it would take time and effort by the administration to provide the food. This happens all too often. Kids want good food and the adults are too busy to provide it. This response by the adminstration should not be taken lightly. If one is not aware of a health problem it is hard to place blame. However, when one is aware, it is the responsibility of the adult to provide for the child. What will it take to bring this problem to the forefront?

The table below is a sample of the bloodwork of kindergarten through fourth graders at a school in the Bronx, New York. Each value can be indicative of early disease.

AA/EPA—results above 11.7 can be indicative of Alzheimers tendencies.

N6/N3—results above 3 can be indicative of tendencies toward cardiovascular and insulin problems.

EPA—The most important fatty acid in the body. The ideal value is 7 or above.

DHA—The most important fatty acid for the brain. The ideal value is 6.

Threshold—Indicative of how well you control the bad fats. The ideal value is less than 1.

EPA+DHA—Indicative of ischemic heart problems. The ideal value is 8.5.

Examples of pre (light blue) and post (yellow) test values in a grade school of K-4 children:

AA/EPA	N6/N3	EPA	DHA	Threshold	EPA+DHA
34.49	8.22	0.33	3.00	104.52	3.33
21.18	6.85	0.53	3.65	39.96	4.18
17.97	7.38	0.73	3.22	24.62	3.95
30.17	6.26	0.52	3.83	58.02	4.35
23.95	6.47	0.49	3.57	48.88	4.06
15.21	4.80	0.74	5.01	20.55	5.75
26.94	4.76	0.45	5.13	59.87	5.58
33.25	7.18	0.35	3.80	95.00	4.15
21.70	5.58	0.52	4.02	41.73	4.54
39.56	5.93	0.31	4.13	127.60	4.44
37.00	12.60	0.28	1.51	132.14	1.79
37.44	9.52	0.33	2.14	113.45	2.47

As can be seen by looking at the above chart, all of the results are outside the normal range. In fact, they are so bad one would think that the school officials would jump at the chance to make sure their students ate well. Instead they ignored the problem. School may be the only place some children can get a hot meal. It is time we take responsibility for our health and that of our children. As these were kindergarteners through fourth graders, blame cannot be placed on the children—it is imperative that adults provide what their beautiful minds and bodies need. It is imperative that schools demand proper nutrition for the children. How much violence will it take to learn the lesson—when will we choose health over disease, love over hate, and peaceful living over violence for all people—KIDS NEED US NOW!!!

LOOK FOR THESE SYMBOLS USED THROUGHOUT THE BOOK...

EASY!	This recipe is easy and can be completed with minimum supervision.
OUCH!	This recipe requires that you use a sharp utensil. Adult supervision is recommended.
HOT!	This recipe requires cooking. Watch out for hot surfaces! Adult supervision is recommended.

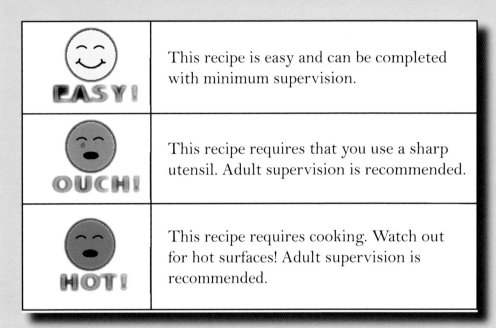

PROTEIN   CARBOHYDRATE   FAT

WANT TO SHARE THIS MEAL?

 MEAL FOR TWO

 MEAL FOR THREE

 MEAL FOR FOUR

THE KEYS TO HEALTHY EATING

BALANCE IS THE MOST IMPORTANT THING TO REMEMBER

Check the Nature's Mighty Bites charts on pages 28-33 to make Mighty Nice choices. If you choose foods from the Mighty Cautious or Mighty Poor categories, make sure you use smaller portion sizes. Balance all your meals like the meal icon at the left. All the recipes in this book are perfectly balanced for you—enjoy without worry!

Be careful when you choose a meal with too many carbohydrates, as Omega-2 will have trouble getting balanced. You will start to lose concentration and focus. You will also want to cheat with fast food!

> I am having trouble hanging on!

This meal is a disaster to your digestive system. Your blood sugar will go way up and will wreak havoc on your concentration and moods. Omega-1 and Omega-3 will be calling out for help!

Besides too much sugar in the food, watch out for the saturated and trans fats. These fats can clog your vessels and contribute to cardiovascular disease. They make you sluggish and compromise your immune system.

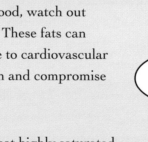

> I can't hang on with all this fat!

> I am having trouble hanging on!

> HELP! Please add some protein!

> Help! I don't like the way caffeine feels

When you eat highly saturated fat meals and add cola drinks with a lot of caffeine, you hurt yourself even more. The constant use of high sugar, high fat, and caffeine leads to many of the problems we have in society today. These are extremely addictive foods! If you don't believe me, just stop eating them for one month and tell me how you feel! How long does it take until you want to run out, buy the food, hide, and eat it?

Powerful Food for Powerful Minds & Bodies   17

The STORY OF NATURE'S MIGHTY BITES™

Once upon a time, in the beautiful hills of Evergreen County, lived a very happy couple named Mr. and Mrs. Mega Bite. They worked very hard and were involved in community affairs, and educational events, and made sure they were available to help those in need.

They assisted at children's sporting games and developed creative educational events for children who found school difficult. Mrs. Mega Bite held parties in her home for

children who didn't like school. Each party would have a theme and an event to help children understand the things they found difficult.

Mrs. Mega Bite noticed that many children didn't eat breakfast and would snack on junk food all day long. She observed that the children who used to enjoy school were

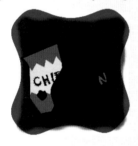

now having trouble. Many of the children who used to be happy were now fighting all the time and were rude to their parents and teachers. She gradually stopped having parties because the children would break things in her house and throw food and drinks all over the furniture. She and Mr. Mega Bite were so unhappy. They so loved to help the children but found it hard to be with them because of their offensive behavior.

One day Mrs. Mega Bite went to the doctor for a checkup and found out she was pregnant. She and her husband were so happy. They would now have their own children and once again be able to have educational parties.

While they were preparing for the birth of their child, they studied many things about health and education. They learned how important it is to eat balanced meals. They began to see why the children they used to work with were having problems. The children were not getting the nutrition they needed to help their minds and bodies work properly. The more the Mega Bites studied, the more they realized how they had contributed to the poor behavior of the children. When they gave the children fast food, the children's behavior changed. When they became too busy to prepare tasty fun foods and bought junk foods, the children had trouble learning.

One day Mr. and Mrs. Mega Bite decided to try an experiment. They invited all the children to their home once again. This time they prepared fun, tasty foods that were nutritious. Their friends, Mrs. Fast Food and Mr. Junk Food, said that none of their children would eat the healthy food. They had tried and tried to get their children to eat vegetables but all they wanted was junk. They soon stopped preparing meals and let them eat whatever they wanted. But Mr. and Mrs. Mega Bite held firm. They prepared the tasty fun food.

All the children were happy to come back to the educational parties. When it came time to go home, all the food had been eaten. Everyone had a great time, and to the parents' surprise, there were no behavior problems, everyone participated in the learning games, and all the children were happy. Even those who always got into trouble were well-behaved.

Now Mr. and Mrs. Mega Bite knew they had a mission in life. Their love for children was so great that they decided to dedicate themselves to the education of children. From their own learning experience they realized that food must be an important part of helping children reach their full potential.

Mr. and Mrs. Mega Bite were excited to have found an answer for such a puzzling dilemma. Finding ways to provide fun, tasty, nutritious foods for kids could help a whole generation of young minds begin to see possibilities and success, rather than failure and hopelessness. The Mega Bites began to read every book they could find about food and soon they became very confused. There were so many different opinions about food. They realized they had to find a way to explain food so everyone could easily understand.

They knew how important it is to be able to understand the basic principles and use them in their own busy daily schedules.

One day they met a scientist who was doing research about the way food worked in the body. They studied long hours and understood what the scientist was saying. There are simple principles of food. If you follow the basic rules you can easily have a healthy body, a happy spirit, and a clear mind.

Mr. and Mrs. Mega Bite were very excited. They knew they had a very important job. They must adapt the basic food principles into their life, learn them well, understand how to apply them, and then they could easily teach others by their example. They had many parties to try out the new principles and found that if they didn't tell their guests they were serving healthy food, everyone ate what was served. They realized that food is a very emotional issue and one that must be dealt with carefully and with loving concern. They now began their journey to bring healthy food to all children and to help parents find easy ways to prepare it.

Mr. and Mrs. Mega Bite were very happy with their new information. They felt good with their new eating style, they had lots of energy, were much more productive, and their minds were clear all day long. They slept great and enjoyed exercising more than when they used to force themselves to do it. They also starting taking time to relax instead of being so busy all the time. They got more done more efficiently and had time left over for play.

Soon the day came for Mrs. Mega Bite to give birth. They would now have a child of their own. The Doctor came to help with the delivery. As the little girl was born, Mr. Mega Bite exclaimed, "O-mega!" Soon it was apparent there was another child on the way, and Mr. Mega Bite exclaimed, "O-mega 2!!" All of a sudden another appeared and they both exclaimed, "O-mega 3!!!" Wow, three children at one time! What an addition to their family! In all the excitement they realized that they had already named their children:
Omega-1, Omega-2 and Omega-3. How great to have three at once. They would now start feeding them balanced from the beginning.

When the excitement of the birth calmed down, Mr. and Mrs. Mega Bite realized they had a wonderful way to teach their own family about food and health. They decided to give each child a role in teaching others. They felt if they started teaching their children right away, it

would become a part of their lifestyle, and easy for them to follow the principles every day. They knew it would be best to work together as a family. They noticed how well-behaved the children were and how quickly they learned new things. All three children loved to be together. When a teacher recommended that the parents separate the children so they could learn new things on their own, Mr. and Mrs. Mega Bite were not happy. Their children were best friends and always wanted to be together. Soon the people of the neighborhood noticed how happy and well-behaved the Mega Bite children were. Their family became known as Mr. and Mrs. Mega Bite and the 3 Mighty Bites.

Soon the Mighty Bites were old enough to take on some responsibility. Mr. and Mrs.

Mega Bite decided to give each one a special role. Omega 1 was put in charge of teaching about Proteins, Omega 2 was put in charge of teaching about Carbohydrates, and Omega 3 was put in charge of teaching about Fats. Each studied very hard to learn all they could about their special topic. They wanted to help others. Their parents felt this would be a perfect job for each of them since they loved to be together all the time and worked best when they were together. Their parents were so proud of them as each became an expert in their own field. Soon it became time to start teaching others. They began their journey to help all children choose fun, delicious food. Many parents were too busy to cook for the family so they decided to help children learn to cook. The Mega Bites found that if they taught children to cook, they could teach them math and reading with the recipes. The children who had found school difficult were having fun learning all kinds of new things. What greater fun than to help your parents cook a meal and then sit down together to eat and discuss the day's activities! The Mighty Bites made a poster to help everyone remember the basic rules of eating and charts to learn how to make the best choices for each meal of proteins, carbohydrates and fats. Then they began their journey to teach all the children of the world how to have powerful minds and powerful bodies.

Let's Get Started

In the next section you will learn:

- The basic rules of eating
- The basic rules of cooking
- How to tell if your food is healthy
- How to read a label
- How to use this book
- How to use the Food Charts

Basic Rules of Eating

1 Always eat within ONE HOUR of getting up.

2 There are three parts to a meal. A PROTEIN, a CARBOHYDRATE and a FAT. Always eat all three parts together at the same time. This keeps you balanced.

3 Eat SMALL MEALS throughout the day. Make sure you eat at least every FIVE HOURS. This keeps your mind and body working efficiently all day long.

4 Always add some ESSENTIAL FATTY ACIDS, especially the long chain Omega-3 fatty acids, to your diet. This is very important because our food no longer has enough. To make it easy add the Nature's Mighty 3s™.

✳ Make sure you get some EXERCISE each day. Choose one you like to do.

✳✳ If you are vegetarian, substitute a vegetarian source of PROTEIN for the menu you choose.

Basic Rules of Cooking

1 Check the recipe. If you need to use a sharp knife and children are helping, teach them to be safe, not sorry. Teach them to ask for help, especially when they don't understand, instead of jumping ahead without knowing what is best to do.

2 Always wash the fruits or vegetables before you use them. Always wash your hands also.

3 Teach the children to use the stove and the oven and any other appliance you may need to use, such as a blender, food processor or even a wire whisk.

4 Read the recipes ahead of time to make sure you have all the ingredients. Plan ahead and make sure to write the ingredients on the shopping list.

5 Teach the children to use the measuring utensils. This will help them in their math classes. They can visually see what they are measuring.

6 Work carefully. To make the cooking experience fun, don't rush. Do one step at a time.

7 Before you cook or bake, reread the instructions to make sure you have done each step! This lets the children practice reading!

8 Clean up after each step. This way you can enjoy the food and not have a big mess to clean up when you are ready to eat or when you get up from the table.

9 After eating, put the dishes in the dishwasher or in the sink to wash. Be careful with glasses and sharp knives.

10 Check the oven, the stove and all the appliances used to make sure they are turned off. Put everything away in its proper place so it can be found next time you cook.

General Cooking Tools

Spatula

Liquid Measure Cups

Measuring Spoons
1 tablespoon
1 teaspoon
1/2 teaspoon
1/4 teaspoon
1/8 teaspoon

Egg Separator

Sharp Knife

Rubber Spatula

Electric Mixer

Blender

Muffin Pan

Cutting Board

Wire Whisk

Saucepans

Grater

Frying/Sauté Pan or Griddle

Mandoline

Eggbeater

Zester

Dry Measuring Cups
1/8 1/4 1/3 1/2 1 Cup

We often think the food we are eating is healthy for us. For example, we have been taught that an apple is a healthy food. Yet an apple by itself is a carbohydrate and breaks down into sugar. Yes, it has minerals and vitamins but the sugar content can outweigh the nutritious side of the food. Eat with a protein and you solve the problem.

GLYCEMIC INDEX

Professors David Jenkins and Tom Wolever at the University of Toronto were the first to introduce material regarding the glycemic index of foods. This numerical index is a system of measuring how fast a carbohydrate triggers a rise in circulating blood sugar. The higher the number, the greater the blood sugar response. A low glycemic index food will cause a small rise, while a high glycemic index food will trigger a dramatic spike. This index only ranks food high in carbohydrates because foods high in fat or protein don't cause a rise in blood sugar.

GLYCEMIC LOAD

Researchers at Harvard University looked at the amount and type of carbohydrates consumed and developed the term "glycemic load." This helps us predict the effect of a particular carbohydrate on our blood glucose level. The glycemic load is calculated by multiplying the glycemic index of a food by the amount of carbohydrate grams per serving and dividing by 100.

SUGAR

We have to be careful with sugar. Looking at the glycemic index, we find that foods we considered healthy, like baked potatoes and cereals, can cause severe insulin spikes. Nature's Mighty Bites™ meals make use of the glycemic index and glycemic load to help keep blood sugar levels under control. This is very important for people with diabetes but also for those who are overweight. Childhood obesity is at a very high level today. Our research has shown that ADD, ADHD, depression, dyslexia and OCD also relate to high levels of sugar intake.

INSULIN CONTROL

Dr. Barry Sears' research has shown that to keep insulin under control—thereby controlling weight gain and health problems—protein, carbohydrates and fat need to be put together at the same time for every meal and every snack. This sounds like a difficult thing to do when you first hear about it, but, the food charts can help you learn how to do this. After a few weeks it will become second nature.

HOW TO READ A LABEL!

Reading the label on prepared foods is very important. The front of the package will use phrases such as "all natural," "100% of Vitamin E and Folic Acid," and "100% Daily Value of Vitamins and Minerals." You probably don't look at the back, where the real truth lies. Even if you do, you must be careful. One patient was looking for a cereal that was low in sugar. What she didn't realize is that all carbohydrates are sugar. When the word sugar is on the label it refers to added sugar, so don't let it fool you. Let's look at a typical label:

Nutrition Facts

Serving Size 1 cup (100g)

Servings per container about 9

Amount Per Serving		
Calories	170	
Calories from Fat	10	
		% Daily Value
Total Fat	1 g	1%
Saturated Fat	0 g	0%
Polyunsaturated Fat	0 g	
Monosaturated Fat	0 g	
Cholesterol	0 mg	0%
Sodium	240 mg	10%
Total Carbohydrate	41 g	14%
Dietary Fiber	5 g	20%
Sugars	20 g	
Other Carbohydrates	16 g	
Protein	4 g	

There is one more fallacy on the label. The typical serving size is 3 times the serving size on the label. Most people who eat cereal eat 3 cups, not the indicated ¾ to 1 cup listed. To get an accurate amount of sugar, subtract the dietary fiber amount from the total carbohydrate count to get the grams of insulin-producing carbohydrate. Then multiply the insulin-producing carbohydrate grams by 3. In the above example this would equal 108 grams. To balance this meal you would need to add about 84 grams of protein. The key to reading a label is to remember the balanced food formula: 7 grams of protein, 9 grams of carbohydrate and 1.5 grams of fat. All labels are measured in grams. The above label is for a popular breakfast cereal, said to be healthy and fortified with vitamins and minerals. Let's analyze how healthy it really is.

If a meal contains 108 grams of carbohydrate, divide the number of grams by 2.3, which is the carbohydrate count of a cube of sugar. Therefore the above breakfast cereal contains the equivalent of 47 sugar cubes. How healthy is this??

TO DETERMINE THE AMOUNT OF INSULIN–PRODUCING CARBOHYDRATE

Total Carbohydrate.................41 grams

Dietary Fiber............................- 5 grams

Insulin–producing......................36 grams / 1 cup

Typical Serving 3 cups.......................3 x 36 =108 grams

108 / 2.3 = 47 sugar cubes equivalent in the above cereal

The information, in the above illustration, was taken from the following sources: www.nal.usda.gov/fnic/foodcomp, 2002 and Netzer, Corinne T. 2003. *The complete Book of Food Counts.*

HOW TO USE THIS BOOK

CHOOSE YOUR RECIPE

Depending on the amount of time you have to prepare your meal, choose a recipe that fits your time schedule. Each recipe is already perfectly balanced for you. This means we have already measured the protein, carbohydrate, and fat portions for your menu. Each recipe in this book is shown in four formats—one serving, two servings, three servings, and four servings with the mathematical proportions already calculated for you.

PREPARE YOUR SHOPPING LIST

When you get ready to go shopping, decide how many people you will be cooking for with each recipe. Look at the shopping list for the menu, and then the number of servings to determine the amount you need to buy.

WORK WITH YOUR HELPERS

When your children help you prepare the meal, it is a perfect time to teach them the components of a meal. They can learn what protein, carbohydrate and fat are by checking with the Nature's Mighty Bites™. They can learn about safety by checking the skill chart and they can learn what utensils to use by checking the "you need" list for the utensils. They can also learn to prepare a shopping list by checking ahead for recipes they would like to try and putting them on the shopping list. They can learn math by measuring the ingredients.

READ FOOD LABELS

Teach your children to read food labels, see page 26. Help them understand the amount of sugar that is in prepared foods. Show them the food charts that depict how many sugar cubes are in the highly advertised commercial foods. You will find these food charts with every recipe section.

SUBSTITUTING INGREDIENTS

If you want to substitute an ingredient be sure to check the food charts: protein on pages 28-29, carbohydrate on pages 30-32, and fat on page 33. When you substitute, just make sure you use the correct measurement. For example, 1/5 cup of rice is the same amount of sugar as 3 cups of cooked broccoli.

BE CREATIVE

Look at the recipes you have been using. Balance them by checking the food charts on pages 28-33. Teach your children to use the charts. You can help them learn math by showing them how to measure, help them read by checking the ingredients of the recipe and teach them to be organized by asking them to be in charge of the shopping list. The family that eats together in a balanced way gets healthy together.

FOOD CHARTS

Each food is broken into units. A typical meal for a child is 2 units of protein, 2 units of carbohydrates, and 2 units of fat. A typical meal for a woman is 3 units of protein, 3 units of carbohydrates, and 3 units of fat. A typical meal for a man is 4 units of protein, 4 units of carbohydrates, and 4 units of fat. A typical meal for an athlete is 5-6 units of protein, carbohydrate and fat.

PROTEIN CHART

Look at the protein chart. Try to eat the Mighty Nice choices. Pick the protein you like. For example, a 1 ounce chicken breast. A child will multiple the 1 ounce by 2, a woman will multiply by 3 and a man will multiply by 4. A child will eat 2 ounces, a woman 3 ounces, a man 4 ounces and an athlete will eat 5-6 ounces..

Meat & Poultry				
Mighty Nice Choices (low in saturated fat)				
These protein choices are low in saturated fat and high in quality protein. Try to get organically raised proteins as they are free of unnecessary hormones. The taste of organic meats is far superior.				
Beef range-fed	1 oz.	Beef, ground range fed	1 1/2 ozs.	Chicken breast skinless	1 oz.
Chicken breast, deli-style	1 1/2 ozs.	Turkey breast, skinless	1 oz.	Turkey breast, deli-style	1 1/2 ozs.
Turkey, ground	1 1/2 ozs.	Knox Gelatin, pkg.	1 pkg.	Venison	1 oz.
Venison, ground	1 1/2 ozs.	Ostrich	1 oz.	Ostrich, ground	1 1/2 ozs.
Buffalo	1 oz.	Buffalo, ground	1 1/2 ozs.	Squab	1 oz.
Pheasant	1 oz.				
Mighty Cautious Choices (moderate in saturated fat)				
These protein choices have more saturated fat. Try to get organically raised protein as they are free of unnecessary hormones. The taste of organic meats is far superior. Try to eat Mighty Nice choices when possible.				
Beef, lean cuts	1 oz.	Beef, ground (less than 10% fat)	1 1/2 ozs.	Chicken, dark meat, skinless	1 oz.
Canadian bacon, lean	1 oz.	Corned beef, lean	1 oz.	Duck	1 1/2 ozs.
Ham, lean	1 oz.	Ham, deli-style	1 1/2 ozs.	Lamb, lean	1 oz.
Lamb, ground	1 oz.	Pork, lean	1 oz.	Pork chop	1 oz.
Turkey dark meat, skinless	1 oz.	Veal	1 oz.		
Mighty Poor Choices (high in saturated fat, arachidonic acid or both)				
These protein choices have more saturated fat. Try to get organically raised protein as they are free of unnecessary hormones. The taste of organic meats is far superior. Try to eat Mighty Nice choices when possible.				
Bacon, pork (strips)	3	Bacon, turkey (strips)	3	Beef, fatty cuts*	1 oz.
Kielbasa	2 ozs.	Beef, ground (10 to 15% fat)	1 1/2 ozs.	Beef, ground (above 15% fat)*	1 1/2 ozs.
Hot dog (pork or beef)	1 link	Hot dog (turkey or chicken)	1 link	Liver, beef*	1 oz.
Liver, chicken*	1 oz.	Pepperoni	1 oz.	Salami	1 oz.
Sausage, pork	2 links	Sausages, pork	1 patty		
*contains arachidonic acid.				

PROTEIN CHART CONTINUED

Fish & Seafood. Mighty Nice Choices

Fish is a great source of protein. However, make sure you get fresh water fish or cold water fish as most fish in the stores are farm raised and therefore very low in the necessary Omega-3 fatty acids.

Bass, freshwater	1 oz.	Bass, sea	1 1/2 ozs.	Bluefish	1 1/2 ozs.
Calamari	2 ozs.	Catfish	1 1/2 ozs.	Clams	1 1/2 ozs.
Cod	1 1/2 ozs.	Crabmeat	1 1/2 ozs.	Haddock	1 1/2 ozs.
Halibut	1 1/2 ozs.	Lobster	1 oz.	Mackerel**	1 1/2 ozs.
Salmon**	1 1/2 ozs.	Sardine**	1 oz.	Scallops	1 1/2 ozs.
Shrimp	1 1/2 ozs.	Snapper	1 1/2ozs.	Sole	1 1/2 ozs.
Trout	1 oz.	Tuna (steak)	1 oz.	Tuna, canned in water	1 oz.

**Rich in EPA

Eggs. Mighty Nice Choices

Egg Whites are one of the best sources of protein. Try to get cage free eggs—the taste is much better and so is the protein quality!

Egg whites (X large)	2	Egg white	1/4 cup		

Mighty Cautious Choices

The problem with egg yolks is that they contain arachidonic acid. It is a fat we must stay away from for good health.

Whole egg* (large)	1	*Contains arachidonic acid.	

Dairy

Dairy is a good source of protein, but try to get organic sources as they free of the unnecessary hormones. Also use low fat dairy sources. The Mighty Poor choices contain a lot of saturated fat.

Mighty Nice Choices

Cheese, non-fat	1 oz.	Cottage cheese, low-fat	1/4 cup	Ricotta cheese, skim	2 ozs.

Mighty Cautious Choices

Cheese, low fat	1 oz.	Mozzarella cheese, skim	1 oz.	

Mighty Poor Choices

Hard Cheeses	1 oz.		

Vegetarian. Mighty Nice Choices

Soy is a great source of protein. It contains no cholesterol or saturated fat and has lots of protein, vitamins, and fiber. It also has a lot of health benefits.

Tofu, firm & extra firm	2 ozs.	Protein powder	1/8 cup	Soy burgers	1/2 patty
Soy hot dog	1 link	Soy sausages	2 links	Soy sausage	1 patty

Protein/Carb Combo. Mighty Nice Choices (Contains one part protein and one part carbohydrate)

Milk, low-fat (1%)	1 cup	Tempeh	1 1/2 ozs.	Tofu, soft	3 ozs.
Yogurt, plain	1/2 cup				

CARBOHYDRATE CHART

Next pick a carbohydrate. Look at the Mighty Nice choices first. For example, to measure the right amount of broccoli, a child would multiply by 2 and eat 10 cups. Wow! That is a lot. So mix and match to equal the number of units you need. A child could choose 2 1/2 cups of broccoli, and add 1/2 cup of green beans. Then add 1/3 cup applesauce for dessert. You can mix and match any carbohydrate. Just make sure you get the number of units you require.

Cooked Vegetables

Mighty Nice Choices

Artichoke (large)	1	Artichoke, hearts	1 cup	Asparagus spears	20
Beans, black	1/3 cup	Beans, green or wax	$1^{1/2}$ cups	Bok choy	7 cups
Broccoli	$3^{1/4}$ cups	Brussels sprouts	1 cup	Cabbage	$2^{1/4}$ cups
Cauliflower	5 cups	Chickpeas	1/4 cup	Collard greens, chopped	$1^{3/4}$ cups
Eggplant	$1^{1/3}$ cups	Kale	2 cups	Kidney beans	1/4 cup
Leeks	$1^{1/4}$ cups	Lentils	1/3 cup	Mushrooms (boiled)	2 cups
Okra, sliced	$2^{3/4}$ cups	Onions, chopped	1/2 cup	Onions, pearled	$1^{1/3}$ cups
Sauerkraut	$3^{1/4}$ cups	Spinach	$3^{1/2}$ cups	Swiss chard, chopped	$2^{1/2}$ cups
Turnip, mashed	$1^{1/3}$ cups	Turnip greens, chopped	7 cups	Yellow squash, sliced	$1^{3/4}$ cups
Zucchini, sliced	2 cups				

Raw Vegetables

Alfalfa Sprouts	21 cups	Bean Sprouts	2 cups	Broccoli	$2^{1/2}$ cups
Cabbage, shredded	$3^{3/4}$ cups	Cauliflower, pieces	$3^{1/4}$ cups	Celery, sliced	$5^{1/2}$ cups
Cucumber	1	Cucumber, sliced	$5^{2/3}$ cups	Endive, chopped	118 cups
Green Pepper	$2^{1/2}$	Red Pepper	2	Green Pepper, chopped	2 cups
Red Pepper, chopped	$1^{1/2}$ cups	Hummus	1/3 cup	Lettuce, iceberg, head	$1^{2/3}$
Lettuce, romaine	14 cups	Mushrooms, chopped	4 cups	Onions, chopped	2/3 cup
Radishes, sliced	$4^{1/4}$ cups	Salsa, check label	3/4 cup	Snow peas	$2^{3/4}$ cups
Spinach, chopped	22 cups	Tomato	$2^{2/3}$	Water chestnuts	1/3 cup

Fruits (fresh, frozen or canned in water)

Apple	1/2	Applesauce	1/3 cup	Apricots	3
Blackberries	$1^{1/2}$ cups	Blueberries	1/2 cup	Boysenberries	$1^{1/2}$ cups
Cantaloupe	1/5	Cantaloupe	3/4 cup	Cherries	9
Fruit cocktail, in water	1/2 cup	Grapefruit	1/2	Grapes (seedless)	1/3 cup
Honeydew melon	2/3 cup	Kiwi fruit (medium)	1	Lemon (small)	2
Lime (medium)	2	Nectarine (medium)	3/4	Orange	1/2
Mandarin Orange, in water	1 cup	Peach	1	Peaches, in water	2/3 cup
Pear	1/2	Pineapple, cubed	1/2 cup	Plum	$1^{1/4}$
Raspberries	1 cup	Strawberries	1 cup	Tangerine	1
Watermelon, cubed	3/4 cup				

Grains

Barley and oats have a lower glycemic index. Oatmeal is a great source of the Omega-6 fatty acid GLA.

Barley (dry)	$1^{1/2}$ tbls.	Oatmeal (slow-cooking)	1/3 cup	Oatmeal, slow-cook, dry	1/4 cup

CARBOHYDRATE CHART CONTINUED

Mighty Cautious (use in moderation)

"Mighty Cautious" carbohydrates, such as breads, grains, pastas, and starches have a high glycemic index. When you choose a Mighty Cautious vegetable or fruit, use smaller portions as they become sugar very quickly.

Cooked Vegetables

Acorn squash	1/2 cup	Baked beans	1/4 cup	Beets, sliced	3/4 cup
Butternut squash	1/2 cup	Carrot, shredded, raw	1 cup	Carrot, sliced	1 cup
Corn	1/4 cup	French fries	6	Lima beans	1/4 cup
Parsnip	1/3 cup	Peas	3/4 cup	Pinto beans	1/3 cup
Potato, baked	1/4	Potato, boiled	1/3 cup	Potato, mashed	1/4 cup
Refried beans	1/3 cup	Sweet potato, baked	1/3	Sweet potato, mashed	1/5 cup

Fruits

Banana	1/3	Cranberries, chopped	1 cup	Cranberry sauce	1 1/2 tsps.
Dates	1 1/2	Fig	1 piece	Guava	3/4 cup
Kumquat	4	Mango, sliced	1/3 cup	Papaya, cubed	3/4 cup
Prunes (dried)	2	Raisins	1 1/2 tbls.		

Fruit Juices

Be very cautious with juice. It becomes sugar very quickly and enters the bloodstream very fast. It is better to eat the fruit!

Apple	1/3 cup	Apple cider	1/3 cup	Cranberry	1/4 cup
Fruit punch	1/4 cup	Grape	1/4 cup	Grapefruit	1/3 cup
Lemon	1/2 cup	Lemonade (unsweetened)	1/4 cup	Orange	1/3 cup
Pineapple	1/4 cup	Tomato	1 cup	V-8	1 cup

Grains, Cereals and Breads

This category produces sugar very quickly. It's best to skip this group unless you use very small amounts!

Bagel (small)	1/4	Biscuit, small	1/2	Bread crumbs	2 tbls.
Bread, whole grain	1/2 slice	Bread, white	1/2 slice	Breadstick, soft	1/2
Breadstick, hard	1/2	Buckwheat, dry	1 1/2 tbls.	Bulgur wheat, dry	1 1/4 tbls.
Cereal, dry	1/3 cup	Cornbread	1" sq.	Cornstarch	4 tsps.
Couscous, dry	1 1/4 tbls.	Cracker, Ak-mak	3	Cracker, saltine	4
Croissant, plain, small	1/2	Crouton	7 tbls.	Doughnut, plain	1/3
English muffin	1/3	Granola	3 tbls.	Grits, cooked	1/4 cup
Melba toast	2	Millet, cooked	1/5 cup	Muffin, blueberry mini	1
Noodles, egg (cooked)	1/4 cup	Noodles, elbow (cooked)	1/4 cup	Pancake (three-inch)	1
Pasta, cooked	1/8 cup	Pita bread, small	1/2 pkt.	Popcorn, air popped	1 1/2 cups
Rice, brown (cooked)	1/5 cup	Rice, white (cooked)	1/5 cup	Rice cake	1
Roll, kaiser	1/4	Roll, dinner (small)	1/2	Roll, hamburger	1/2
Taco shell (small)	1	Tortilla, corn (six-inch)	1	Tortilla, flour (8")	1/3
Waffle	1/3				

CARBOHYDRATE CHART CONTINUED

Others					
Watch these items very carefully. If you want ice cream, eat Nature's Mighty Bites™ Ice Cream and you won't have to worry! It's balanced and tastes great!					
Barbecue sauce	5 tbls.	Cake (small slice)	1/4 slice	Candy bar	1/4
Cocktail sauce	5 tbls.	Cookie (small)	1	Honey	1/2 tbls.
Ice cream, regular	1/4 cup	Ice cream, premium	1/6 cup	Jam or jelly	2 tsps.
Ketchup	2 1/2 tbls.	Molasses, light	1 1/2 tsps.	Plum sauce	1 tbls.
Potato chips	1/2 oz.	Pretzels	1/3 oz.	Relish, pickle	4 tsps.
Sugar, brown	3 tsps.	Sugar, granulated	2 tsps.	Sugar, confectionery	1 tbls.
Syrup, maple	2 tsps.	Syrup, pancake	2 tsps.	Teriyaki sauce	3 tbls.
Tortilla chips	1/2 oz.				

TIP

All carbohydrates are sugar. Your body needs sugar but only in small amounts. Make sure sugar is balanced with protein.

TIP

Choose "Mighty Nice" carbohydrates because you can have more of them. They have a lower glycemic load (fewer sugar cubes).

TIP

All juices are very high in sugar. This causes insulin to be released and lowers the blood sugar. This negates the nutritional value of fruit.

TIP

High fiber vegetables and fruits give us the necessary vitamins and minerals we need each day. Choose ones you like and enjoy.

FAT CHART

Next pick a fat. You could use oil to cook the chicken, add slivered nuts to the vegetables, or make a sauce to put over the vegetables.

Mighty Nice (rich in mono-unsaturated fat)					
There are two types of good fats, monounsaturated, and long-chain Omega-3 fats. Monounsaturated fats come from olive oil, selected nuts and avocados. Long-chain omega-3 fats come from fish and fish oils.					
Almond butter	1/2 tsp.	Almonds (slivered)	1 1/3 tsp.	Almonds (whole)	3
Avocado	3/4 tbls.	Cashews	3	Guacamole	3/4 tbls.
Macadamia nut	1	Olive oil	1/3 tsp.	Olive oil/vinegar dressing (1/3 tsp. olive oil, 1/3 tsp. vinegar)	1 tsp.
Peanut oil	1/3 tsp.	Peanut butter, natural	1/2 tsp.		
Olives	5	Tahini	1/2 tsp.	Canola oil	1/3 tsp.
Peanuts	3				
Mighty Cautious Choices (low in saturated fat)					
These are contain saturated fats. Use them with caution!					
Mayonnaise, light	1 tsp.	Mayonnaise, regular	1/3 tsp.	Soybean oil	1/3 tsp.
Sesame oil	1/3 tsp.	Pecans	2	Pecan Butter	1/3 tsp.
Walnuts	2	Walnuts, chopped	1 tsp.	Walnut Butter	1/3 tsp.
Mighty Poor Choices (rich in saturated fat)					
These contain saturated fats. Be really careful of trans fats, and arachidonic acid. Whenever you see the words "partially hydrogenated vegetable oil" you know it is a bad fat. If rabbits have arachidonic acid injected into them, they will die in three minutes. These fats with a really big name needs to be eliminated from your diet. Stay away from them.					
Bacon bits (imitation)	2 tsps.	Butter	1/3 tsp.	Cream (half & half)	3/4 tbls.
Cream cheese	1 tsp.	Cream cheese, light	1 3/4 tsps.	Lard	1/3 tsp.
Sour cream	1/2 tbls.	Sour cream, light	1 tbls.	Vegetable shortening	1/3 tsp.
Hard Margarine	Don't eat	Soft Margarine	Don't eat		

TIP

Monounsaturated fats are very important for good health. The best choices are nuts such as almonds, cashews and macadamia nuts.

TIP

Extra-light olive oil, avocados and guacamole are also great mono-unsaturated fats. Remember fat does not make you fat.

FOOD IS OUR FRIEND BUT CAN BE OUR ENEMY!!

Childhood obesity is growing at alarming rates. Depression, ADD, ADHD, and violent behavior are the topics of conversation when many speak about the youth of today. The remedy is usually drugs, boot camp, more discipline, etc., but very few talk about the role that food plays in these paramount problems. It isn't the amount of food these children or adults eat—it is the combination and the quality of the foods they are eating that is so very important.

LEARNING THE SCIENCE OF FOOD

In 1996 I met Dr. Barry Sears. I had been doing research for about 16 years regarding the immune system and diet. After hearing his lecture, I realized that I had overlooked a very important biochemical principle. In order to maintain good health, insulin must be controlled. If insulin is stimulated and pushes the blood sugar too low, the result is hypoglycemia. If the insulin is too low and the blood sugar gets too high, the result is hyperglycemia or eventually full-blown diabetes. The problems seem overwhelming yet the correction is simple. Dr. Sears' research shows that if you control the ratio of protein to carbohydrate in every meal and eat every five hours you solve the insulin issue that can cause so many biochemical and immune related problems.

As I applied these principles in the treatment plan for my patients, those who complied got better very quickly. The ratio was based on scientific principles related to the body's need for a balance of protein, carbohydrate and fat. When I applied these principles both to my diet and my patients' diets I noticed the following:

Control of appetite
Control of insulin and balanced blood sugar levels
Greater concentration
Ability to stay on task

The body requires protein, carbohydrate and fat for biological and hormonal efficiency. The benefits of eating a balanced meal are almost immediate. When insulin is stable, blood sugar is stabilized, and cravings are controlled and become nonexistent.

PROTEIN

Protein is important for rebuilding cells and systems of the body. Muscle, the immune system, and every enzyme in the body is made up of protein. Every day protein is used and lost, so unless we add adequate dietary protein, important body functions begin to run down.

It is important to eat adequate amounts of protein for your body size, yet do not eat too much protein, for excess protein turns to body fat. Too little leads to protein malnutrition. The human body can only handle about 6 ounces maximum per meal. A 6 ounce portion would be the amount of protein required by an athlete or someone who does strenuous activities throughout the day. An easy way to know how much protein is right for you is to look at the palm of your hand. That is roughly the size of the piece of protein you should be eating. Small amounts of protein throughout the day enable the body to work efficiently, as long as you have adequate amounts of carbohydrate to balance the protein and thereby balance your hormonal activity.

CARBOHYDRATE

Eating "Mighty Nice" carbohydrates, in the form of fruits and vegetables, is the body's way to balance the protein intake. Carbohydrates act as a powerful drug—too many cause an overproduction of insulin and can lead to sluggish feelings and the storage of body fat. All carbohydrates become sugar. Our bodies need a certain amount of sugar to work efficiently. However, excess carbohydrates lead to excess sugar and disease can follow. To balance, the protein, use fiber-rich fruits and vegetables.

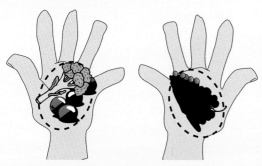

An easy way to remember how much to eat is to have two handfuls of vegetables and fruit. If you choose complex carbohydrates that produce more sugar, eat an amount equal to the protein portion.

When looking at carbohydrates, it is important to look at not only the carbohydrate grams, but the glycemic index and the glycemic load. The faster glucose enters the bloodstream, the more insulin you make, and the more problems you have.

Some complex carbohydrates, such as potatoes, rice and carrots, enter the bloodstream faster than table sugar. It is important to understand the effect of any carbohydrate source on insulin. The glycemic load takes into account the density of the carbohydrate plus the rate of entry into the bloodstream. The glycemic load shows the explosive effect of the sugar entering the bloodstream. The higher the glycemic load, the more insulin is affected and the more dangerous is the effect of that particular meal on normal body function.

FAT

The third component of a meal is fat. Fat has no effect on insulin but it does slow down the rate of entry of carbohydrates into the bloodstream. Fat also causes the body to release the hormone cholecystokinin (CCK) from the stomach. CCK is the hormone that goes to the brain to deliver the message to stop eating. By eating monounsaturated fat you have the primary switch to stop overeating. This doesn't mean you should eat all kinds of fat, but rather you need a constant amount of polyunsaturated fats. These are the building blocks of the most important hormone of the body, the eicosanoids. These hormones control every cell, every organ, and every system of the body. When the eicosanoids are under control, the body is healthy, and when they are out of control, disease occurs.

The most important type of fat to eat is monounsaturated fat—it is a hormonally neutral fat and it tastes great. The amount of food ratio depends on body weight and intensity of daily activity.

BALANCED MEAL

Let's compare a typical breakfast for an American child. In my research over the past 22 years, I found that a high percentage of children leave home in the morning without eating breakfast. If they do eat breakfast, they eat a meal consisting mainly of complex carbohydrates. The cereal box calls one serving one cup of cereal. However, by polling over 75 families, I found a typical serving is 3 cups or more! Most parents want their children to eat a healthy meal and the advertising world would like us to believe that

they have a healthy product. I once visited a cereal manufacturing plant with a friend of mine and saw that the box that is advertised as "vitamin enriched" means that in the process of filling the box, powdered vitamins and minerals are added to the box. They tend to fall to the bottom and are in the dust that very few eat. One of the instructors in the undergraduate college I attended, and head of the biochemistry department, did a research study to show that the cardboard of the box actually contained more nutrition than the contents in the box.

As the commercial states, "Where's the beef?" Most, if not all, cereals consist only of carbohydrates which break down into sugar. "But," you say, "the meal also contains toast and orange juice." Once again, all carbohydrates are sugar. So, where is the protein?

FIVE MEALS A DAY!

When you eat food in a balanced way you will be surprised how your appetite is controlled, you will not overeat, and concentration levels remain constant along with your energy levels. This can sound very confusing when you first start but there is an easier way to determine how to eat. If you always take your hands with you every place you go, you will always know how to eat. Look at your hands, and choose your portions. If you choose Mighty Nice protein, vegetables and fruits, you see that you can have much bigger portions and keep insulin levels constant while Mighty Cautious and Mighty Poor Carbohydrates need to be kept small as they have a much higher glycemic index and glycemic load. Your five fingers tell you to eat five meals a day and go no longer than five hours between meals. So always take your hands with you everywhere you go, then before you eat, look at your hands and pick your foods. Easy!

OMEGA-3 FATTY ACIDS

Omega-3 fatty acids are essential for good health. Our bodies do not make EPA and DHA to maintain good health, so the essential fatty acids must come from our diet. However we do not get enough from the North American diet so we need to take fish oil in supplement form. Fish contain EPA/DHA, however, the majority of the fish eaten today are farm raised and contain only small amounts of the long-chain Omega-3 essential fatty acids. We don't need to supplement our diet with the Omega-6 fatty acids, as we get plenty from foods that contain corn, safflower, sunflower or soybean oils. In fact it is very important to watch the ratio of the Omega-6 to Omega-3 fatty acids. Research shows that the optimum ratio is 1 to 1. It has been shown that the general population tends to show a ratio from 6 to 1 to as high as 25 to 1. Therefore it is now recommended to decrease Omega-6 and increase Omega-3 intake. The finding of the prestigious *Journal of Clinical Metabolism* states that "lack of Omega-3 fatty acids may be the biggest nutritional deficiency in the North American diet."

WHY FISH OIL?

Our food sources today are severely lacking in the Omega-3 fatty acids. Omega-3 fatty acids are called essential fatty acids because they are essential to good health. Early ancestors had a diet rich in the Omega-3 and Omega-6 fatty acids. Most of the fats in the typical North American diet come from foods heavily laden with "trans fats" found in foods processed by hydrogenation methods, further increasing our deficiency in Omega-3s. Research has finally shown the importance of EPA (eicosapentaenoic acid) and DHA (docosahexaenoic acid) to maintaining good health. Diets deficient in these long-chain Omega-3 fatty acids, such as extremely low-fat diets, have been shown to be harmful to health. While short-chain Omega-3s can be found in some vegetable oil, such as canola and flaxseed oil, these must be converted by your body to EPA and DHA to obtain the maximal health benefits of these oils. Even if your body had a maximum conversion efficiency, only about 4% ends up as DHA. Therefore the best way to add these important long-chain Omega-3s (EPA and DHA) to your diet is by eating fatty fish two or three times a week and by taking Omega-3 EPA/DHA dietary supplements.

HOW CAN I TAKE IT?

In April 1999, the consensus of a National Institutes of Health conference was that the recommended dose is 3 grams of the long-chain Omega-3 fatty acids per day. You can take:

- 3 1000 mg. 40/20 capsules per day, or 6 1000 mg. 18/12 capsules per day or
- Two teaspoons pharmaceutical grade liquid fish oil per day.

You can purchase Nature's Mighty 3s™ liquid fish oil at www.kidsneedusnow.org or by calling toll-free 1-866-497-8273.

WHAT ABOUT FLAXSEED OIL?

Some flaxseed oils are a good source of Omega-3 fatty acids; however, they are not a good source of the long-chain Omega-3 fatty acids, EPA and DHA. Flaxseed oil is a good source of a short-chain fatty acid, such as alpha-linolenic acid. Short chain fatty acids are converted into EPA and DHA in the body. However, this conversion process is very inefficient, so a large amount of short-chain fatty acid is needed to produce a small amount of long-chain fatty acid. You need to consume 30 grams of flaxseed oil to maybe make 1 gram of EPA and 0.1 gram of DHA.. Fish oil is far superior, as it already contains large amounts of the essential Omega-3 fatty acids, EPA and DHA.

WHY SHOULD WE CHOOSE PHARMACEUTICAL GRADE FISH OIL?

Two factors contribute to the dosage of Omega-3 EPA/DHA: 1) serving size and 2) the concentration of the oil. The higher the concentration, the smaller the serving size required to provide an equal quantity of Omega-3 EPA/DHA. For example, the label of a health food store brand lemon flavored fish oil, the dosage is defined as a teaspoon (approximately 5000 mg. of fish oil). They claim that a teaspoon equals 800 mg. EPA and 500 mg. DHA. Therefore, we know that the oil in this product, is an 18/12 EPA/DHA oil and not a concentrate. Since Nature's Mighty 3s™ is twice as concentrated, it takes only 1/2 teaspoon to get the same amount of EPA/DHA. Another factor to consider is that health-food store grade fish oil is usually distilled to the 10,000th while pharmaceutical grade oil is distilled to the 3,000,000th. This removes the PCBs, mercury and other impurities.

HOW IMPORTANT ARE OMEGA-3 FATTY ACIDS?

Numerous studies have shown health benefits associated with long-chain Omega-3 fish oil include:

HEART - decreases triglycerides up to 30%, reduces blood clotting, lowers blood pressure, decreases blood viscosity, and reduces the development of arrhythmia.

BRAIN - reduces the risk of brain disorders, improves memory, enhances cognition, awareness and mood.

PREGNANCY - the Omega-3 fatty acids, especially DHA, are essential for healthy, well-functioning nervous systems, brains and eyes. It is especially important during the last three months of pregnancy, and the first six months after birth.

IMMUNE SYSTEM - lessens inflammation in the joints and muscles, and increases natural levels of anti-inflammatory agents.

WHAT DOES NATURE'S MIGHTY 3S™ LIQUID FISH OIL TASTE LIKE?

A breath of fresh mint! Nature's Mighty 3s™ is one of the purest and best tasting fish oil yet produced. No odor, smell or taste of fish oil.

WOULD YOU EVER GUESS...

These foods are considered healthy, yet when we look at the grams of carbohydrate, (all carbohydrates become sugar), the glycemic index, and the glycemic load, it presents a different picture. Will you still eat them??? If you are tempted, just put this picture on your refrigerator and see yourself putting sugar cubes in a bowl. Then see if that is what you want to eat.

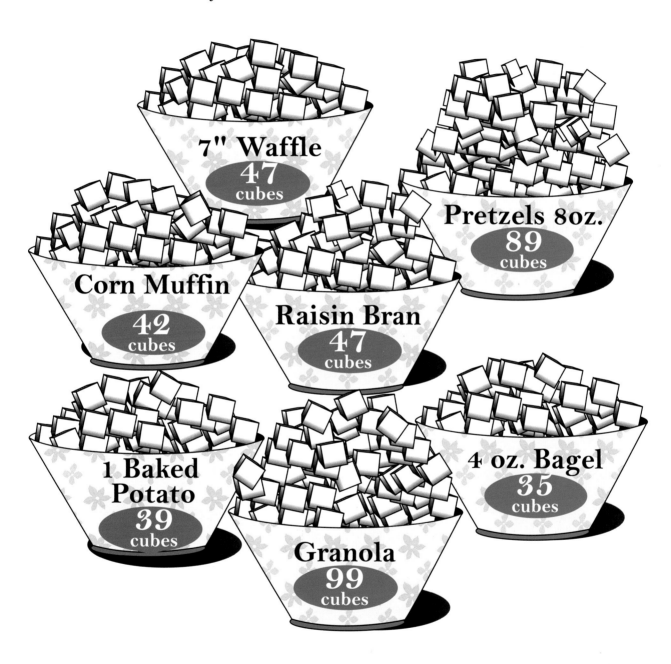

7" Waffle
47 cubes

Pretzels 8oz.
89 cubes

Corn Muffin
42 cubes

Raisin Bran
47 cubes

1 Baked Potato
39 cubes

Granola
99 cubes

4 oz. Bagel
35 cubes

BREAKFAST

Breakfast is the most important meal of the day. When we eat a balanced meal, it helps us wake up, clear our thinking, and start the day's activities. If we are too busy to eat, our body is compromised. It needs fuel to get started each day. A fast–food breakfast doesn't help our body's need for nutrients. Soon, we crave candy and doughnuts.

If you are in a hurry and skip breakfast, your blood sugar drops and you will not be able to concentrate for the day's activities. Not only will this make you hungry, you will also lose a lot of energy in the morning hours. When your blood sugar drops, you get tired and cranky. Children fall asleep in school or get in trouble because they can't control their emotions. Adults in the workplace get irritable.

Breakfast can be exciting, healthy and satisfying. The following recipes have been tested for efficiency, taste, and easy preparation. Enjoy!

Breakfast foods should give you all the energy you need to start the day. Breakfast can be fun and different. If you don't like eggs, cereal, or pancakes, make different choices! You can have a piece of chicken for your protein, some fruit for your carbohydrate, and some nuts for your fat. Be creative!

ASK FOR HELP !

 Ask Omega 1 to help you find your protein.

 Ask Omega 2 to help you balance your carbohydrate.

 Ask Omega 3 to help you add the proper type of fat!

 All the recipes in this book are perfectly balanced for you.

The **FOLLOWING CHARTS** can help you make well–informed decisions regarding your meals. Look carefully, as you may be surprised when you see what you thought was healthy can be the very reason you or a family member may be experiencing some health problems.

SECRET CODES

See if you can investigate which secret codes are in your favorite foods.

= 1 gram protein	= 1 gram saturated fat
= 1 gram total fat	= 1 gram monounsaturated fat
= 5 grams sugar	= excess sugar
= glycemic load	= 1 gram excess fat
= trans fat	= 50 milligrams sodium

"Rev Up" Your Engine!

Our bodies are highly evolved instruments. They need to be fueled properly and often. There are certain rules that we must follow to allow our body to work efficiently. Balance is the major rule of all physiology. Protein activates glugacon in our bodies and helps build strong muscles. Carbohydrates activate insulin and control sugar so it is important we take in exactly the right amount. Fat activates the eicosanoids which control all communication and activities of the body. All three are required at the same time, in different amounts, but in a finely controlled balance, to make sure we function at top efficiency. Would you put one teaspoon of sugar in the gas tank of your car? If you did, you would ruin your engine. We must be careful not to overload our bodies with too much sugar, or we set up the environment inside our bodies for multiple health problems. Too much protein can cause muscle breakdown and too much bad fat can clog our blood vessels. The following charts help us realize what it is we are doing to our body. Remember, we have only one body; there are no replacements!

NATURE'S MIGHTY BALANCED

When you balance a meal according to your dietary needs, the chart will always look like those below. Try the recipes to see that creative, healthy food can be very tasty and fun.

A typical healthy meal for a child contains 14 grams of low fat protein, 18 grams of carbohydrate (8 sugar cubes), and 3 grams of monounsaturated fat. This provides the nutrition needed to build healthy bodies and allows for greater concentration and behavior control. When you use high fiber carbohydrates, the sugar equivalent is even less.

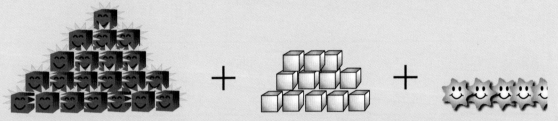

A typical healthy meal for a woman contains 21 grams of low fat protein, 27 grams of carbohydrates (12 sugar cubes), and 4.5 grams of monounsaturated fat. It is always important to control insulin. Balanced foods with the addition of the essential fatty acids controls hormones. When you use high fiber carbohydrates, the sugar equivalent is even less.

A typical healthy meal for a man contains a balance of 28 grams of low fat protein, 36 grams of carbohydrate (16 sugar cubes), and 8 grams of monounsaturated fat and keeps insulin under control. This allows for greater concentration, focus, and mental acuity throughout the day. When you use high fiber carbohydrates, the sugar equivalent is even less.

GETTING ON THE RIGHT TRACK

Nature's Mighty Bites™ Power Pancakes are a perfect balanced breakfast. According to our taste testers, the taste, consistency and presentation are great and the breakdown of ingredients presents a balance of protein, carbohydrate and fat. This meal will provide fullness and satisfaction for at least 4 ½ hours and allow for alertness, energy, and mental focus. Be sure to check other breakfast foods in the breakfast section.

Nature's Mighty Bites™ Pancakes	6 cakes with topping

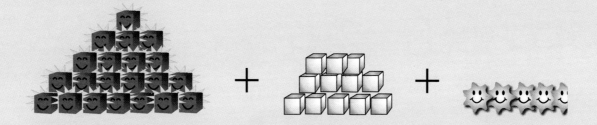

Nature's Mighty Bites™ Protein Powered Oatmeal is another example of a balanced breakfast. Balancing a meal biochemically and hormonally not only makes it healthy, but gives the body the power to fight disease.

Nature's Mighty Bites™ Oatmeal	1 serving (child)

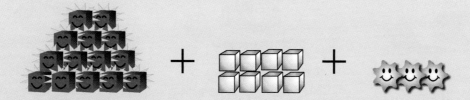

All the recipes were developed for taste and ease of preparation, and many can be made in larger quantities so you have left-overs for other meals. The recipes are simple and can be prepared quickly. Most of the recipes are made for one person, but the calculations are provided for two, three and four servings. Follow the recipe exactly when you first make the meal so you can see what a balanced meal feels like. Then, if you want to make substitutions, check with Nature's Mighty Bites™ and their specific food charts to pick the right proportions. You can always add herbs and spices to satisfy your taste buds. Just make sure there is no hidden sugar in the bottle!

IS THIS WHAT YOU WANT FOR BREAKFAST???

The typical American breakfast amounts to nothing more than a big bowl of sugar! A balanced breakfast should have the correct ratio of protein to carbohydrate. The following chart shows the equivalent of sugar cubes in many breakfasts. How do you start your day?

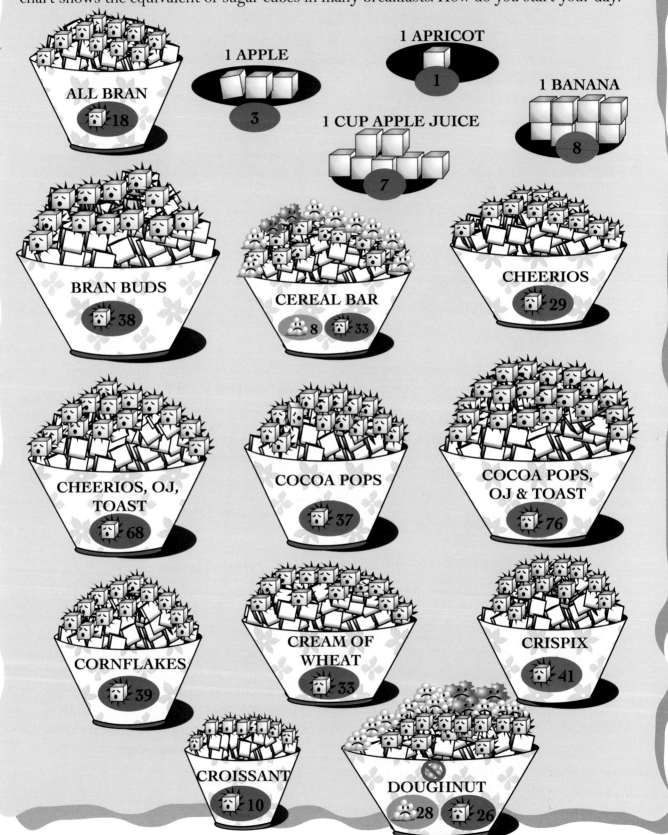

ALL BRAN — 18

1 APPLE — 3

1 APRICOT — 1

1 BANANA — 8

1 CUP APPLE JUICE — 7

BRAN BUDS — 38

CEREAL BAR — 8, 33

CHEERIOS — 29

CHEERIOS, OJ, TOAST — 68

COCOA POPS — 37

COCOA POPS, OJ & TOAST — 76

CORNFLAKES — 39

CREAM OF WHEAT — 33

CRISPIX — 41

CROISSANT — 10

DOUGHNUT — 28, 26

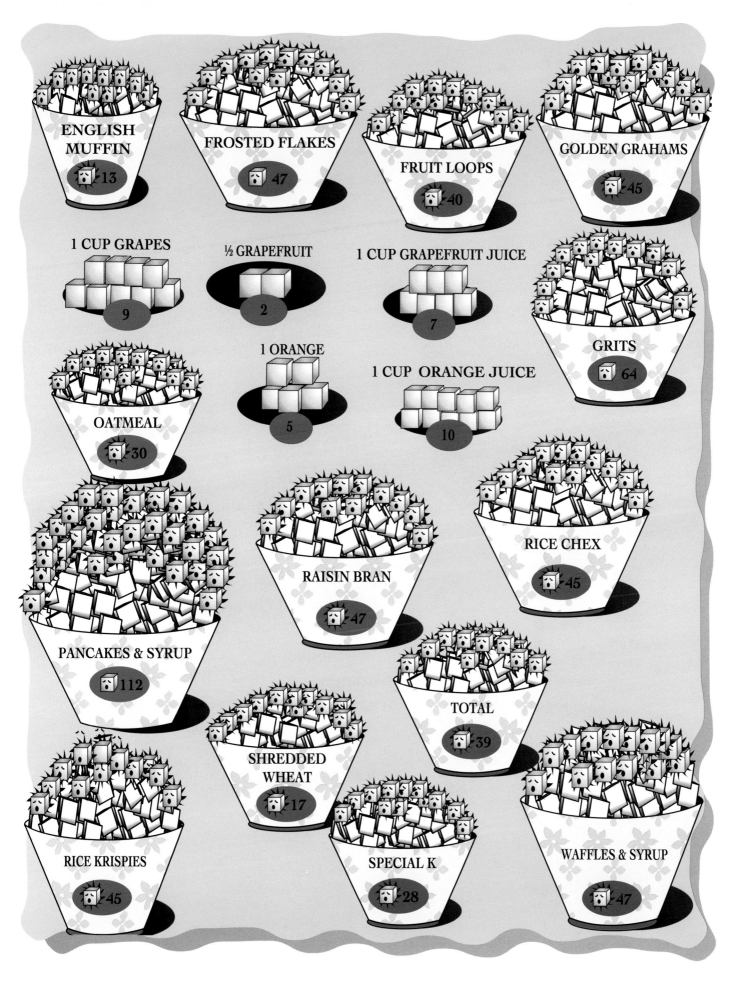

ENGLISH MUFFIN 13

FROSTED FLAKES 47

FRUIT LOOPS 40

GOLDEN GRAHAMS 45

1 CUP GRAPES 9

½ GRAPEFRUIT 2

1 CUP GRAPEFRUIT JUICE 7

GRITS 64

OATMEAL 30

1 ORANGE 5

1 CUP ORANGE JUICE 10

PANCAKES & SYRUP 112

RAISIN BRAN 47

RICE CHEX 45

SHREDDED WHEAT 17

TOTAL 39

RICE KRISPIES 45

SPECIAL K 28

WAFFLES & SYRUP 47

Powerful Food for Powerful Minds & Bodies 45

EGGS & FRUIT BREAKFAST

You need:
2 small bowls
small sharp knife
spatula
frying pan
measuring cups
measuring spoons

Shopping List

egg whites
low-fat cheddar cheese
cantaloupe
orange
grapefruit
sliced peaches
extra-light olive oil

1/4 cup egg white
1 ounce low-fat shredded cheddar cheese

1 slice cantaloupe
1/4 orange
1/4 grapefruit
1/3 cup sliced peaches, fresh or frozen

2/3 teaspoon extra-light olive oil

 Cut the fruit into bite-sized pieces, put in a small bowl and set aside.

 Mix the cheese and egg whites together in a small bowl.

 Pour the olive oil into a frying pan, and warm over medium heat.

 Pour in the egg mixture. Stir gently with a spatula, moving the eggs as they cook.

 Cook to the consistency that you like.

 Serve with the fruit.

SHARE THIS MEAL WITH FRIENDS AND FAMILY

Ingredients			
egg whites	½ cup	¾ cup	1 cup
low fat cheddar cheese	2 ounces	3 ounces	4 ounces
cantaloupe	2 slices	3 slices	4 slices
orange	½ orange	¾ orange	1 orange
grapefruit	½ grapefruit	¾ grapefruit	1 grapefruit
sliced peaches	⅔ cup	1 cup	1⅓ cups
extra-light olive oil	1⅓ teaspoons	2 teaspoons	2⅔ teaspoons

HERB AND FRUIT OMELET

You need:
2 small bowls
spatula
sauté pan
measuring cups
measuring spoons

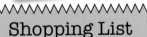

Shopping List

low fat ricotta cheese
grated parmesan cheese
egg whites
snow peas
broccoli
grapes
extra-light olive oil
cashews
chopped chives
black pepper

 1/8 cup low fat ricotta cheese
2 teaspoons grated parmesan cheese
3 egg whites

 1 1/3 cup snow peas
1 1/4 cup broccoli
1/3 cup grapes

 1/3 teaspoon extra-light olive oil
3 cashews

 PLUS! 1 teaspoon chopped chives
pinch black pepper

EASY! HOT!

 1   Mix together the cheese and seasonings in a small bowl. Set aside.

 2   Whisk the eggs in a small bowl until a little bubbly.

 3   Heat the olive oil. Gently sauté the snow peas and broccoli. When finished, spoon them onto a plate.

 4   Pour the eggs into the same pan, but do not stir in the pan. Cook over medium to low heat. When the eggs start to set, sprinkle with cheese, herbs, broccoli and snow peas on one half of the omelet.

 5   When the eggs are cooked, remove the pan from the heat. Using a spatula, fold one half of the omelet over the other.

 6   Serve fruit and nuts with the omelet.

SHARE THIS MEAL WITH FRIENDS AND FAMILY

Ingredients			
low fat ricotta cheese	¼ cup	⅜ cup	½ cup
parmesan cheese	4 teaspoons	2 tablespoons	8 teaspoons
egg whites	6	9	12
snow peas	2⅔ cups	4 cups	5⅓ cups
broccoli	2½ cups	3¾ cups	5 cups
grapes	⅔ cup	1 cup	1⅓ cups
extra-light olive oil	⅔ teaspoon	1 teaspoon	1⅓ teaspoons
cashews	6	9	12
chopped chives	2 teaspoons	1 tablespoon	4 teaspoons
black pepper	2 pinches	3 pinches	4 pinches

YOGURT & FRUIT

PREP TIME: 5 MINUTES

 1/2 cup low fat plain yogurt

 1/8 cup whey protein powder

 1/2 cup fresh strawberries
1/4 cup red grapes

 2 2/3 teaspoons slivered almonds

PLUS! 5 drops liquid stevia, to add sweetness○

You need:
small bowl
mixing spoon
measuring cups
measuring spoons

 Place the yogurt in a bowl.

 Mix the whey protein powder with the yogurt. Add 5 drops of stevia. Mix.

 Slice the strawberries. Mix the strawberries and grapes into the yogurt.

 Sprinkle the nuts on top.

Shopping List
low fat plain yogurt
whey protein powder
fresh strawberries
red grapes
slivered almonds
stevia

○ To find the stevia supplement, see page 200.

SHARE THIS MEAL WITH FRIENDS AND FAMILY

Ingredients			
low fat plain yogurt	1 cup	1 1/2 cups	2 cups
whey protein powder	1/4 cup	3/8 cup	1/2 cup
fresh strawberries	1 cup	1 1/2 cups	2 cups
red grapes	1/2 cup	3/4 cup	1 cup
slivered almonds	5 1/3 teaspoons	8 teaspoons	10 2/3 teaspoons
stevia	10 drops	15 drops	20 drops

MIGHTY MELON

PREP TIME: 5 MINUTES

 ½ cup cottage cheese

 ½ cantaloupe

 2⅔ teaspoons slivered almonds

You need:
small sharp knife
measuring cups
measuring spoons

Shopping List

cottage cheese
cantaloupe
slivered almonds

TIP A melon is ripe when it smells like a melon at the spot on the skin where the stem is attached. If it doesn't smell delicious, better wait a day!

 Cut the cantaloupe in half. Throw the seeds away.

 Put the cottage cheese into the center of the cantaloupe. Sprinkle the nuts on top.

SHARE THIS MEAL WITH FRIENDS AND FAMILY

Ingredients	👫	👫	👪
cottage cheese	1 cup	1½ cups	2 cups
cantaloupe	1	1½	2
slivered almonds	5⅓ teaspoons	8 teaspoons	10⅔ teaspoons

PROTEIN POWERED OATMEAL

PREP TIME: 5 MINUTES
COOK TIME: 15 MINUTES

You need:
sauce pan
measuring cups
measuring spoons
frying pan
wire whisk

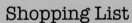
Shopping List
Canadian bacon
whey protein powder
slow cooking oats
slivered almonds
extra-light olive oil
cinnamon

 2 ounce Canadian bacon or
1/4 cup whey protein powder

 2/3 cup dry slow cooking oats

 2 2/3 teaspoons slivered almonds
1/3 teaspoon extra-light olive oil if using
Canadian bacon

 PLUS! 1 1/3 cups water
Sprinkle cinnamon for extra flavor

 If you expect to be in a hurry in the morning, mix the slow cooking oats, protein powder and Nature's Mighty 3s™ together and put in a thermos bottle. Add boiling water and mix thoroughly. Tighten, let set all night. You will have cooked oatmeal in the morning.!

HOT!

 1. Bring the water to boil in a saucepan.

 2. Using a wire whisk, stir the oat mixture into the boiling water.

 3. Reduce to a simmer. Cook for 10-15 minutes to your desired consistency.

 4. If using whey protein powder, blend in when finished cooking. If using the Canadian Bacon, put 1 teaspoon extra-light olive oil in a frying pan, add the bacon and cook.

 5. If you want to add milk use 1%, or nut milk. Use just enough to make a thinner cereal, approximately 1 tablespoon.

 6. Sprinkle with nuts and serve warm.

SHARE THIS MEAL WITH FRIENDS AND FAMILY

Ingredients			
Canadian bacon	4 ounces	6 ounces	8 ounces
whey protein powder	½ cup	¾ cup	1 cup
slow cooking oats	1⅓ cups	2 cups	2⅔ cups
slivered almonds	5⅓ teaspoons	8 teaspoons	10⅔ teaspoons
extra-light olive oil	⅔ teaspoon	1 teaspoon	1⅓ teaspoons
water	2⅔ cups	4 cups	5⅓ cups
cinnamon	2 sprinkles	3 sprinkles	4 sprinkles

FRUIT SALAD

EASY!

 1/2 cup cottage cheese

 1 cup fresh strawberries
1/3 cup green grapes
1/3 cup red grapes

 2²/₃ teaspoons slivered almonds

PLUS! 5 drops liquid stevia, to add sweetness⊙

1 Put the cottage cheese into a small bowl. Add 5 drops stevia. Mix thoroughly.

2 Slice the strawberries. Add to the cottage cheese.

3 Sprinkle the nuts on top.

⊙ To find the stevia supplement, see page 200.

You need:
small bowl
small sharp knife
measuring cups
measuring spoons

Shopping List
cottage cheese
fresh strawberries
green grapes
red grapes
slivered almonds
stevia

SHARE THIS MEAL WITH FRIENDS AND FAMILY

Ingredients	👥	👥	👥👥
cottage cheese	1 cup	1½ cups	2 cups
fresh strawberries	2 cups	3 cups	4 cups
green grapes	2/3 cup	1 cup	1⅓ cups
red grapes	2/3 cup	1 cup	1⅓ cups
slivered almonds	5⅓ teaspoons	8 teaspoons	10²/₃ teaspoons
stevia	10 drops	15 drops	20 drops

NUT BUTTER & APPLES

PREP TIME: 8 MINUTES

EASY! OUCH!

You need:
small bowl
small sharp knife
measuring cups
measuring spoons

Shopping List
whey protein powder
apples
nut butter

 ¼ cup whey protein powder

 1 apple, cut across the core

 1 teaspoon nut butter

 PLUS! 1 tablespoon pure water

 In a small bowl, mix together the whey protein powder, water, and nut butter, until smooth.

 Core the apple to make a doughnut shape. Slices across to make 6 doughnut slices.

 Spread the nut butter mixture on each of the apple slices.

SHARE THIS MEAL WITH FRIENDS AND FAMILY

Ingredients	👥	👥	👥👤
whey protein powder	½ cup	¾ cup	1 cup
apples	2	3	4
nut butter	2 teaspoons	1 tablespoon	4 teaspoons
pure water	⅛ cup	3 tablespoons	¼ cup

FRENCH TOAST

You need:
small bowl
small sharp knife
wire whisk
frying pan
measuring cups
measuring spoons

Shopping List
egg whites
Canadian bacon or
turkey bacon
whole grain bread
fresh strawberries
powdered sugar
extra-light olive oil
slivered almonds

1 2 egg whites
1 ounce extra-lean Canadian bacon or
3 strips turkey bacon

2 1/2 slice whole grain bread ✿
1 cup sliced fresh strawberries
1/8 teaspoon powdered sugar

3 1/3 teaspoon extra-light olive oil
1 1/3 teaspoons slivered almonds

French Meadow Bakery:
Men's Bread
Women's Bread

EASY! OUCH! HOT!

Our french toast is balanced and tastes great! You can even make it before you go to school.

 Beat the egg whites in a small bowl with a wire whisk. Cut the bread into strips. Soak in the egg white mixture.

 Put the oil on the pan. Turn the burner on to medium heat.

 Cook the bread strips, turning often until done.

 Top with sliced strawberries and slivered almonds. Sprinkle the powdered sugar on top.

 Cook the Canadian bacon and serve on the side.

SHARE THIS MEAL WITH FRIENDS AND FAMILY

Ingredients	👤👤	👤👤	👤👤 👤
egg whites	4	6	8
Canadian bacon **or**	2 ounces	3 ounces	4 ounces
turkey bacon	6 strips	9 strips	12 strips
whole grain bread	1 slice	1½ slices	2 slices
fresh strawberries	2 cups	3 cups	4 cups
powdered sugar	¼ teaspoon	⅜ teaspoon	½ teaspoon
extra-light olive oil	⅔ teaspoon	1 teaspoon	1⅓ teaspoons
slivered almonds	2⅔ teaspoons	4 teaspoons	5⅓ teaspoons

POWER PANCAKES

PREP TIME: 10 MINUTES
COOK TIME: 8 MINUTES

You need:
measuring cups
measuring spoons
pancake griddle
2 small bowls

Shopping List
lowfat buttermilk
whey protein powder
egg whites
oat flour
barley flour
extra-light olive oil
vanilla extract
salt
baking powder
stevia
applesauce
cinnamon
strawberries
blueberries
strawberry essence
macadamia nuts
real maple syrup

 1 cup low fat buttermilk

 ³/₄ cups whey protein powder
¹/₄ cup egg whites

 ³/₄ cup oat flour
¹/₄ cup barley flour*

 1 tablespoon extra light olive oil

 PLUS!
1 tablespoon vanilla extract
¹/₂ teaspoon salt
1 tablespoon baking powder to make light
5 drops liquid stevia ✿

To find barley flour, check a health food store or go on-line (see appendix for web sites). You can use whole wheat flour; but barley is better. It is low glycemic and tastier.

✿ *To find the stevia supplement, see page 200.*

EASY! HOT!

Our pancakes are balanced, not like those on page 45.

 Mix all dry ingredients together (whey protein powder, oat flour, barley flour, baking powder, and salt).

 Mix all wet ingredients (buttermilk, egg whites, olive oil, vanilla extract and stevia).

 Mix wet and dry ingredients, until well-blended. Do not over-mix.

 Put 1 teaspoon olive oil on the griddle. Turn on medium heat. If a drop of water sizzles when dropped on the griddle, it is ready.

 Put ⅛ cup batter, per pancake, on the griddle. When bubbles come through the pancake it is ready to flip. Makes 18-20 three inch pancakes.

Pick The Topping			
Mix the ingredients and drizzle on the waffles			
Apple Cinnamon	Strawberry	Blueberry	Macadamia Maple
⅓ cup unsweetened applesauce	½ cup chopped strawberries	¼ cup blueberries	2 tsps. real maple syrup
⅛ tsp. cinnamon	2 tbls. unsweetened applesauce	2 tbls. unsweetened applesauce	½ tsp. finely ground macadamia nuts
1 tbls. water	½ tsp. strawberry essence	½ tsp. strawberry essence	Grind the nuts to a sticky paste..
Mix together and put on top.	Mix together and put on top.	Mix together and put on top.	Blend with the maple syrup.

SHARE THIS MEAL WITH FRIENDS AND FAMILY

Ingredients	👥	👥	👥👤
lowfat buttermilk	2 cups	3 cups	4 cups
whey protein powder	1½ cups	2¼ cups	3 cups
egg whites	½ cup	¾ cup	1 cup
oat flour	1½ cups	2¼ cups	3 cups
barley flour	½ cup	¾ cup	1 cup
extra-light olive oil	⅛ cup	3 tablespoons	¼ cup
vanilla extract	⅛ cup	3 tablespoons	¼ cup
salt	1 teaspoon	1½ teaspoons	2 teaspoons
baking powder	⅛ cup	3 tablespoons	¼ cup
stevia✿	10 drops	15 drops	20 drops

MIGHTY NICE WAFFLES

PREP TIME: 10 MINUTES
COOK TIME: 8 MINUTES

You need:
2 small bowls
small sharp knife
spatula
waffle iron
measuring cups
measuring spoons

Shopping List
low-fat buttermilk
whey protein powder
egg whites
oat flour
barley flour
strawberries
powdered sugar
extra-light olive oil
salt
vanilla extract
baking soda
baking powder
stevia
applesauce
cinnamon
strawberries
blueberries
strawberry essence
macadamia nuts
real maple syrup

³/4 cup low fat buttermilk

³/4 cup whey protein powder
¹/4 cup egg whites

³/4 cup oat flour
¹/4 cup barley flour*
1 cup sliced strawberries
2 teaspoons powdered sugar

3 tablespoons extra light olive oil

PLUS!
¹/2 teaspoon salt
1 tablespoon vanilla extract
1 teaspoon baking soda
2 teaspoons baking powder
5 drops liquid stevia ✪

*To find barley flour, check a health food store or go on-line (see appendix for web sites). You can use whole wheat flour; barley is better. It is low glycemic and tastier.

✪ To find the stevia supplement, see page 200.

I feel balanced when I eat these. I don't when I eat the ones on page 45.

 Mix all dry ingredients together (**whey protein powder, oat flour, barley flour, baking soda, baking powder, and salt**).

 Mix all wet ingredients (buttermilk, egg whites, olive oil, vanilla and stevia). Mix wet and dry ingredients, until well-blended. Do not over-mix.

 Brush oil onto a waffle iron. Pour batter on the center of the lower half. Close the lid. When the waffle is browned, about 3-4 minutes, it is finished. The next ones will take about 2-3 minutes.

 Top each with some strawberries and dust with powdered sugar, or make a topping.

Pick The Topping
Mix the ingredients and drizzle on the waffles

Apple Cinnamon	Strawberry	Blueberry	Macadamia Maple
1/3 cup unsweetened applesauce	1/2 cup chopped strawberries	1/4 cup blueberries	2 tsps. real maple syrup
1/8 tsp. cinnamon	2 tbls. unsweetened applesauce	2 tbls. unsweetened applesauce	1/2 tsp. finely ground macadamia nuts
1 tbls. water	1/2 tsp. strawberry essence	1/2 tsp. strawberry essence	Grind the nuts to a sticky paste..
Mix together and put on top.	Mix together and put on top.	Mix together and put on top.	Blend with the maple syrup.

SHARE THIS MEAL WITH FRIENDS AND FAMILY

Ingredients	👥	👥	👥👥
low fat buttermilk	1½ cups	2¼ cups	3 cups
whey protein powder	1½ cups	2¼ cups	3 cups
egg whites	1/2 cup	3/4 cup	1 cup
oat flour	1½ cups	2¼ cups	3 cups
barley flour	1/2 cup	3/4 cup	1 cup
sliced strawberries	2 cups	3 cups	4 cups
powdered sugar	4 teaspoons	1/8 cup	8 teaspoons
extra-light olive oil	6 tablespoons	9 tablespoons	3/4 cup
salt	1 teaspoon	1½ teaspoons	2 teaspoons
vanilla extract	1/8 cup	3 tablespoons	1/4 cup
baking soda	2 teaspoons	1 tablespoon	4 teaspoons
baking powder	4 teaspoons	2 tablespoons	8 teaspoons
stevia	10 drops	15 drops	20 drops

MIGHTY NICE PANCAKE & WAFFLE TOPPINGS

APPLE CINNAMON TOPPING

Ingredients	🧍🧍	🧍🧍🧍	🧍🧍🧍🧍
unsweetened applesauce	⅔ cup	1 cup	1⅓ cups
cinnamon	¼ teaspoon	½ teaspoon	¾ teaspoon
water	2 tablespoons	3 tablespoons	4 tablespoons

Put the applesauce in a small bowl. Add the cinnamon and water and mix thoroughly. Spread over the pancakes.

BLUEBERRY SAUCE TOPPING

Ingredients	🧍🧍	🧍🧍🧍	🧍🧍🧍🧍
blueberries	½ cup	¾ cup	1 cup
unsweetened applesauce	¼ cup	6 tablespoons	½ cup
strawberry essence	1 teaspoon	1½ teaspoons	2 teaspoons

Put the blueberries in a small bowl. Add the applesauce and strawberry essence and mix thoroughly. Spread over the pancakes.

STRAWBERRY SAUCE TOPPING

Ingredients	🧍🧍	🧍🧍🧍	🧍🧍🧍🧍
strawberries	1 cup	1½ cups	2 cups
unsweetened applesauce	¼ cup	6 tablespoons	½ cup
strawberry essence	1 teaspoon	1½ teaspoons	2 teaspoons

Put the strawberries in a small bowl. Add the applesauce and strawberry essence and mix thoroughly. Spread over the pancakes.

MACADAMIA MAPLE SYRUP TOPPING

Ingredients	🧍🧍	🧍🧍🧍	🧍🧍🧍🧍
real maple syrup	4 teaspoons	2 tablespoons	8 teaspoons
macadamia nuts	1 teaspoon	1½ teaspoons	2 teaspoons

Grind the nuts in a food processor until they make a sticky paste. Add the maple syrup and blend. Spread over the pancakes.

SHAKES

Shakes are a great choice for breakfast, lunch, dinner or snacks. They are fast to make and go down easily in the morning. There are as many variations as your imagination creates!

Substitutions in the recipes are simple:

- Change the **fruit** to one you like better. Check with **Omega-2** to find a "Mighty Nice" fruit, or if you choose a "Mighty Cautious" one, be sure you measure the correct portion.

- **Replace** the **milk** with an equal amount of **nuts and/or nut milk.**

- Use **skim milk** for the liquid if you prefer it to nut milk.

- Use **soy protein powder** instead of whey, or mix it half and half.

- Replace the banana with ½ **cup favorable fruit**, such as **peaches** or ¼ **cup blueberries**.

- Extra-light **olive oil** makes the shake creamy and has no olive taste.

Getting ready is easy:

- Peel a banana and cut into 1" or 2" chunks.

  Freeze the chunks in a plastic bag. This way you'll always have them ready for shakes.

- Make your favorite nut milk ahead. Keep it in the refrigerator to use for shakes.

- Purchase frozen fruit. Get extra to have on hand ready for quick shakes.

- *If you want more sweetness in your shake add 5 drops, of the nuritional supplement, stevia. The best we have found is made by Astraya. To order call 1-800-867-7258.

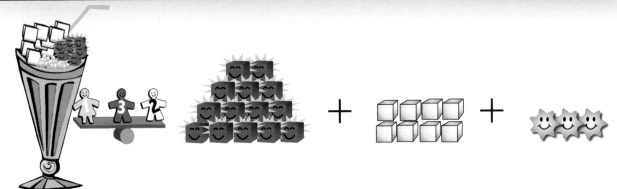

A typical healthy shake contains 14 grams of low fat protein, 18 grams of carbohydrates, and 3 grams of monounsaturated fat. This gives the nutrition needed to build healthy bodies and allows for greater concentration and behavior control.

What are YOU Eating?

CAUTION! CHECK THE LABELS!

The following charts analyze some of the popular sport drinks that are advertised as being healthy. Let's see how they compare to a Nature's Mighty Bites™ Shake (above)! What you will see is the ratio of protein, carbohydrate and fat. They may have protein, but are they balanced?

 P=Protein   F=Fat

C=Carbohydrate   S=Sodium
SC=Sugar Cube

 Boost, High Protein Vanilla
P - 15 g
SC - 12
(C - 33 g)
F - 6 g
S - 170 mg

Boost, Vanilla
P - 15 g
SC - 13
(C - 33 g)
F - 6 g
S - 170 mg

 Ensure, High Protein Vanilla
P - 12 g
SC - 8
(C - 31 g)
F - 9 g
S - 290 mg

Ensure Vanilla
P - 9 g
SC - 12
(C - 40 g)
F - 5 g
S - 22 mg

NUT MILK

PREP TIME: 8 MINUTES

Where Are My Brother And Sister? Make Sure You Add A Protein And A Carbohydrate To Make This Complete!

1 cup slivered almonds, cashews or macadamia nuts, all without skin

PLUS! 5 cups purified water

1 Puree the nuts with 2 cups of spring water until smooth.

2 Add 3 more cups water. Blend until the mixture is very smooth.

3 Strain through an extra fine strainer or a layer of cheesecloth. Press the solids to retrieve all the nut milk. Discard the solids.

You need:
measuring cups
blender

Shopping List
nuts
spring water

TIP Put in the refrigerator to keep cold. This will make a lot of milk for shakes or you can use it in place of milk in any recipe.

EXTRA IDEAS!:

If you are allergic to milk or want added flavor, use nut milk instead of 1% milk. If you roast the nuts you get extra flavor!

PEACHY CREAM SHAKE

EASY!

PREP TIME: 5 MINUTES

You need:
measuring cups
measuring spoons
blender

 1/4 cup whey protein powder

 2/3 cup fresh or frozen peaches

 2 2/3 teaspoons slivered almonds
1 cup nut milk

PLUS! 1/4 teaspoon vanilla extract
5 drops liquid stevia, to add sweetness ✿

 Blend the fruit, and almonds in a blender until they are in little pieces.

 Add the whey protein powder, nut milk, vanilla, and stevia.

 Add 1 cup of chopped ice.

 Blend until smooth.

✿ To find the stevia supplement, see page 200.

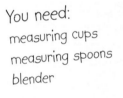

Shopping List

whey protein powder
fresh or frozen peaches
slivered almonds
nut milk
vanilla extract
stevia

SHARE THIS MEAL WITH FRIENDS AND FAMILY

Ingredients			
whey protein powder	1/2 cup	3/4 cup	1 cup
fresh or frozen peaches	1 1/3 cups	2 cups	2 2/3 cups
slivered almonds	5 1/3 teaspoons	8 teaspoons	10 2/3 teaspoons
nut milk	2 cups	3 cups	4 cups
vanilla extract	1/2 teaspoon	3/4 teaspoon	1 teaspoon
stevia	10 drops	15 drops	20 drops
chopped ice	2 cups	3 cups	4 cups

PEANUTTY SHAKE

PREP TIME: 5 MINUTES

You need:
measuring cups
measuring spoons
blender

 1 1/8 cup whey protein powder
1/3 cup silken tofu

 2 1/3 frozen banana
1/3 cup fresh or frozen peach slices

 3 1/2 cup nut milk
1/4 teaspoon natural peanut butter

PLUS! 5 drops liquid stevia, to add sweetness✪

1 Pureé the fruit in a blender until it is in little pieces.

2 Add the whey protein powder, nut milk, silken tofu, stevia, and peanut butter.

3 Add 1 cup of chopped ice.

4 Blend until smooth.

✪ To find the stevia supplement, see page 200.

Shopping List

whey protein powder
silken tofu
bananas
fresh or frozen peaches
nut milk
natural peanut butter
stevia

SHARE THIS MEAL WITH FRIENDS AND FAMILY

Ingredients	👥	👥	👥👤
whey protein powder	1/4 cup	3/8 cup	1/2 cup
silken tofu	2/3 cup	1 cup	1 1/3 cups
bananas	2/3	1	1 1/3
peach slices	2/3 cup	1 cup	1 1/3 cups
nut milk	1 cup	1 1/2 cups	2 cups
peanut butter	1/2 teaspoon	1 teaspoon	1 1/2 teaspoons
stevia	10 drops	15 drops	20 drops
chopped ice	2 cups	3 cups	4 cups

RASPBERRY SHAKE

EASY!

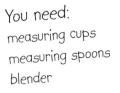

You need:
measuring cups
measuring spoons
blender

 1 cup 1% milk

 ⅛ cup whey protein powder

 1 cup fresh or frozen raspberries

 ⅔ tablespoon extra-light olive oil

 ¼ teaspoon vanilla extract
5 drops liquid stevia, to add sweetness✪

 Pureé the fruit in a blender until it is in little pieces.

 Add the milk, oil, stevia, vanilla, and protein powder.

 Add 1 cup of chopped ice.

 Blend until smooth.

✪ To find the stevia supplement, see page 200.

Shopping List

1% milk
whey protein powder
fresh or frozen raspberries
extra-light olive oil
vanilla extract
stevia

SHARE THIS MEAL WITH FRIENDS AND FAMILY

Ingredients	👥	👥	👥👤
1% milk	2 cups	3 cups	4 cups
whey protein powder	¼ cup	⅜ cup	½ cup
raspberries	2 cups	3 cups	4 cups
extra-light olive oil	1⅓ teaspoons	2 teaspoons	2⅔ teaspoons
vanilla extract	½ teaspoon	¾ teaspoon	1 teaspoon
stevia	10 drops	15 drops	20 drops
chopped ice	2 cups	3 cups	4 cups

BERRY BANANA SHAKE

EASY!

You need:
measuring cups
measuring spoons
blender

 ¼ cup whey protein powder

 1 cup fresh or frozen strawberries
⅓ frozen banana

 ⅓ teaspoon extra-light olive oil
1 cup nut milk

PLUS! ¼ teaspoon vanilla extract
5 drops liquid stevia, to add sweetness❁

1 Pureé the fruit in a blender until it is in little pieces.

2 Add the nut milk, oil, stevia, and whey protein powder.

3 Add 1 cup of chopped ice.

4 Blend until smooth.

❁ To find the stevia supplement, see page 200.

Shopping List

whey protein powder
fresh or frozen strawberries
bananas
extra-light olive oil
nut milk
vanilla extract
stevia

SHARE THIS MEAL WITH FRIENDS AND FAMILY

Ingredients	👥	👥	👥👤
whey protein powder	½ cup	¾ cup	1 cup
strawberries	2 cups	3 cups	4 cups
bananas	⅔	1	1⅓
extra-light olive oil	⅔ teaspoon	1 teaspoon	1⅓ teaspoons
nut milk	2 cups	3 cups	4 cups
vanilla extract	½ teaspoon	¾ teaspoon	1 teaspoon
stevia	10 drops	15 drops	20 drops
chopped ice	2 cups	3 cups	4 cups

SUNSHINE SHAKE

EASY!

PREP TIME: 5 MINUTES

You need:
measuring cups
measuring spoons
blender

 ¼ cup whey protein powder

 ⅔ frozen banana
2 tablespoons fresh or frozen lemon juice

 ¾ teaspoon nut butter
¾ cup nut milk

PLUS! ½ teaspoon lemon essence.
5 drops liquid stevia, to add sweetness❂

 Pureé the fruit in a blender until it is in little pieces.

 Add the nut milk, lemon juice, whey protein powder, and stevia.

 Add 1 cup of chopped ice.

 Blend until smooth.

❂ To find the stevia supplement, see page 200.

Shopping List
whey protein powder
bananas
fresh or frozen lemon juice
nut butter
nut milk
lemon essence
stevia

SHARE THIS MEAL WITH FRIENDS AND FAMILY

Ingredients	👥	👥	👥👤
whey protein powder	½ cup	¾ cup	1 cup
bananas	1⅓	2	2⅔
lemon juice	¼ cup	6 tablespoons	½ cup
nut butter	1½ teaspoons	2¼ teaspoons	3 teaspoons
nut milk	1½ cups	3 cups	4½ cups
lemon essence	1 teaspoon	1½ teaspoons	2 teaspoons
stevia	10 drops	15 drops	20 drops
chopped ice	2 cups	3 cups	4 cups

BLUEBERRY SHAKE

EASY!

 1 cup 1% milk

 1/8 cup whey protein powder

 1/3 frozen banana
1/2 cup blueberries, fresh or frozen

 2/3 teaspoon extra-light olive oil

PLUS! 1 teaspoon vanilla extract
5 drops liquid stevia, to add sweetness✿

 Pureé the fruit in a blender until it is in little pieces.

 Add the milk, whey protein powder, olive oil, stevia, and vanilla.

 Add 1 cup of chopped ice.

 Blend until smooth.

✿ To find the stevia supplement, see page 200.

You need:
blender
measuring cups
measuring spoons

Shopping List

1% milk
whey protein powder
bananas
fresh or frozen blueberries
extra-light olive oil
vanilla extract
stevia

SHARE THIS MEAL WITH FRIENDS AND FAMILY

Ingredients	👬	👬	👬👧
1% milk	2 cups	3 cups	4 cups
whey protein powder	1/4 cup	3/8 cup	1/2 cup
bananas	2/3	1	1 1/3
blueberries	1 cup	1 1/2 cups	2 cups
extra-light olive oil	1 1/3 teaspoons	2 teaspoons	2 2/3 teaspoons
vanilla extract	2 teaspoons	1 tablespoon	4 teaspoons
stevia	10 drops	15 drops	20 drops
chopped ice	2 cups	3 cups	4 cups

BERRY LIME SHAKE

PREP TIME: 5 MINUTES

EASY!

You need:
blender
measuring cups
measuring spoons

 ½ cup 1% low fat milk
¼ cup low fat plain yogurt

 ⅛ cup whey protein powder

 1 cup fresh or frozen raspberries
juice of ½ lime

 ⅔ teaspoon extra-light olive oil

PLUS! 5 drops liquid stevia, to add sweetness✿

 Pureé the fruit in a blender until it is in little pieces.

 Add the milk, yogurt, protein powder, raspberries, lime juice, olive oil, and stevia.

 Add 1 cup of chopped ice.

 Blend until smooth.

✿ To find the stevia supplement, see page 200.

Shopping List

1% low fat milk
low fat plain yogurt
whey protein powder
fresh or frozen raspberries
limes
extra-light olive oil
stevia

SHARE THIS MEAL WITH FRIENDS AND FAMILY

Ingredients			
1% lowfat milk	1 cup	1½ cups	2 cups
low fat plain yogurt	½ cup	¾ cup	1 cup
whey protein powder	¼ cup	⅜ cup	½ cup
raspberries	2 cups	3 cups	4 cups
lime juice	1 lime	1½ limes	2 limes
extra-light olive oil	1⅓ teaspoons	2 teaspoons	2⅔ teaspoons
stevia	10 drops	15 drops	20 drops
chopped ice	2 cups	3 cups	4 cups

CREAMY ORANGE SHAKE

PREP TIME: 8 MINUTES

EASY!

 ½ cup 1% milk

 ⅛ cup whey protein powder

 ⅓ cup sliced peaches, fresh or frozen
⅓ cup orange juice

 ⅔ teaspoon extra-light olive oil

PLUS! 1 teaspoon grated orange rind
5 drops liquid stevia, to add sweetness✿

1 Blend fruit and juice with the orange rind.

2 Add the 1% milk, whey protein powder, olive oil, and stevia to the blender.

3 Add 1 cup of chopped ice.

4 Blend until smooth.
✿ To find the stevia supplement, see page 200.

You need:
blender
measuring cups
measuring spoons
zester or food grater

Shopping List

1% milk
whey protein powder
fresh or frozen sliced peaches
orange juice
extra-light olive oil
orange rind
stevia

SHARE THIS MEAL WITH FRIENDS AND FAMILY

Ingredients	👥	👥	👥👤
1% milk	1 cup	1½ cups	2 cups
whey protein powder	¼ cup	⅜ cup	½ cup
sliced peaches	⅔ cup	1 cup	1⅓ cups
orange juice	⅔ cup	1 cup	1⅓ cups
extra-light olive oil	1⅓ teaspoons	2 teaspoons	2⅔ teaspoons
grated orange rind	2 teaspoons	1 tablespoon	4 teaspoons
stevia	10 drops	15 drops	20 drops
chopped ice	2 cups	3 cups	4 cups

TROPICAL SHAKE

PREP TIME: 5 MINUTES

EASY!

1/8 cup whey protein powder
1/3 cup silken tofu

1/3 cup fresh orange juice
1/4 cup frozen pineapple pieces
1/3 cup frozen peach slices

1/2 cup nut milk
2/3 tablespoon extra-light olive oil

PLUS!
1/2 teaspoon lemon essence
5 drops liquid stevia, to add sweetness❂

Pureé the fruit in a blender until it is in little pieces.

Add the protein powder, silken tofu, orange juice, nut milk, oil, lemon essence, and stevia.

Add 1 cup of chopped ice.

Blend until smooth.

❂ To find the stevia supplement, see page 200.

You need:
blender
measuring cups
measuring spoons

Shopping List

whey protein powder
silken tofu
fresh orange juice
frozen pineapple pieces
peach slices
nut milk
extra-light olive oil
lemon essence
stevia

SHARE THIS MEAL WITH FRIENDS AND FAMILY

Ingredients	👬	👬	👬👤
whey protein powder	1/4 cup	3/8 cup	1/2 cup
silken tofu	2/3 cup	1 cup	1 1/3 cups
fresh orange juice	2/3 cup	1 cup	1 1/3 cups
pineapple pieces	1/2 cup	3/4 cup	1 cup
peach slices	2/3 cup	1 cup	1 1/3 cups
nut milk	1 cup	1 1/2 cups	2 cups
extra-light olive oil	1 1/3 teaspoons	2 teaspoons	2 2/3 teaspoons
lemon essence	1 teaspoon	1 1/2 teaspoons	2 teaspoons
stevia	10 drops	15 drops	20 drops
chopped ice	2 cups	3 cups	4 cups

VERY BERRY SHAKE

EASY!

You need:
blender
measuring cups
measuring spoons

 ¼ cup whey protein powder

 1½ cup fresh or frozen blackberries
½ cup fresh or frozen blueberries

 1 cup nut milk
⅔ teaspoon extra-light olive oil

PLUS! ¼ teaspoon vanilla extract
5 drops liquid stevia, to add sweetness✿

 Pureé the fruit in a blender until it is in little pieces.

 Add the whey protein powder, nut milk, olive oil, vanilla extract, and stevia.

 Add 1 cup of chopped ice.

 Blend until smooth.

✿ To find the stevia supplement, see page 200.

Shopping List

whey protein powder
fresh or frozen blackberries
fresh or frozen blueberries
extra-light olive oil
vanilla extract
stevia

SHARE THIS MEAL WITH FRIENDS AND FAMILY

Ingredients	👫	👫👤	👫 👤
whey protein powder	½ cup	¾ cup	1 cup
blackberries	3 cups	4½ cups	6 cups
blueberries	1 cup	1½ cups	2 cups
nut milk	2 cups	3 cups	4 cups
extra-light olive oil	1⅓ teaspoons	2 teaspoons	2⅔ teaspoons
vanilla extract	½ teaspoon	¾ teaspoon	1 teaspoon
stevia	10 drops	15 drops	20 drops
chopped ice	2 cups	3 cups	4 cups

VERY CHERRY SHAKE

PREP TIME: 5 MINUTES

EASY!

 ¼ cup low fat plain yogurt
½ cup low fat milk

 ⅛ cup whey protein powder

 9 fresh or frozen cherries

 ⅔ teaspoon extra-light olive oil

PLUS! ¼ teaspoon vanilla extract
5 drops liquid stevia, to add sweetness○

 Pureé the fruit in a blender until it is in little pieces.

 Add the whey protein powder, olive oil, nut milk, vanilla extract, and stevia.

 Add 1 cup of chopped ice.

 Blend until smooth.

○ To find the stevia supplement, see page 200.

You need:
blender
measuring cups
measuring spoons

Shopping List

low fat plain yogurt
low fat milk
whey protein powder
fresh or frozen cherries
extra-light olive oil
vanilla extract
stevia

SHARE THIS MEAL WITH FRIENDS AND FAMILY

Ingredients			
low fat plain yogurt	½ cup	¾ cup	1 cup
low fat milk	1 cup	1½ cups	2 cups
whey protein powder	¼ cup	⅜ cup	½ cup
cherries	18	27	36
extra-light olive oil	1⅓ teaspoons	2 teaspoons	2⅔ teaspoons
vanilla extract	½ teaspoon	¾ teaspoon	1 teaspoon
stevia	10 drops	15 drops	20 drops
chopped ice	2 cups	3 cups	4 cups

STRAWBERRY KIWI SHAKE

EASY!

 ½ cup low fat plain yogurt

 ⅛ cup whey protein powder

 ½ kiwi, peeled and sliced
½ cup sliced strawberries, fresh or frozen

 ⅔ teaspoon extra-light olive oil

PLUS! ½ teaspoon vanilla extract
5 drops liquid stevia, to add sweetness✿

 Pureé the fruit in a blender until it is in little pieces.

 Add yogurt, whey protein powder, olive oil, vanilla, and stevia.

 Add 1 cup of chopped ice.

 Blend until smooth.

✿ To find the stevia supplement, see page 200.

You need:
blender
measuring cups
measuring spoons

Shopping List

low fat plain yogurt
whey protein powder
kiwis
strawberries
extra-light olive oil
vanilla extract
stevia

SHARE THIS MEAL WITH FRIENDS AND FAMILY

Ingredients			
low fat plain yogurt	1 cup	1½ cups	2 cups
whey protein powder	¼ cup	⅜ cup	½ cup
kiwis	1	1½	2
sliced strawberries	1 cup	1½ cups	2 cups
extra-light olive oil	1⅓ teaspoons	2 teaspoons	2⅔ teaspoons
vanilla extract	1 teaspoon	1½ teaspoons.	2 teaspoons
stevia	10 drops	15 drops	20 drops
chopped ice	2 cups	3 cups	4 cups

LUNCH

Lunch is an important meal. You refuel for the afternoon and stabilize your blood sugar. When you eat a healthy lunch you can concentrate, stay calm and happy, and when school is out, you feel energetic enough to have fun with your friends.

Be Creative with Lunch to make it fun!

⭐ To make school lunches fun, find a creative, colorful and convenient lunch box.

⭐ Use a sturdy Thermos bottle for liquids. Make sure the Thermos bottle is suitable for both hot and cold liquids.

⭐ Make unique lunches so your child will not be tempted to eat the heavy, starchy school lunches loaded with sugar, saturated and trans fats.

⭐ Check out the school lunch menu and see if you can make the same thing in a balanced way with healthy ingredients.

Getting ready is easy:

⭐ Make special treats on the weekend to put in the lunch box.

⭐ Use leftovers from special dinners.

⭐ Get the lunch ready the night before so if you oversleep you will still be ready.

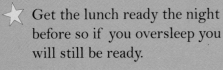

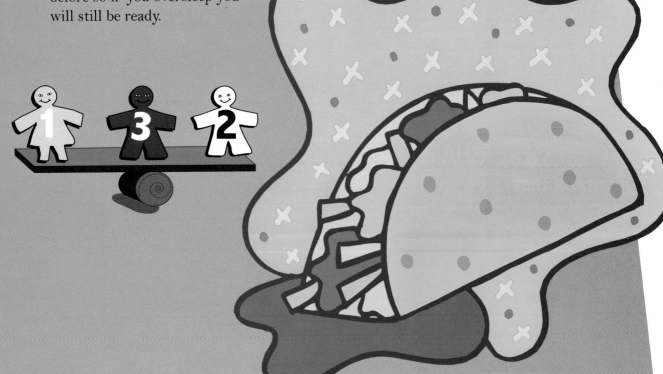

The Adventures of Nature's Mighty Bites

SATAY SAUCE

EASY!

When you use this recipe make sure you check with Omega 1 to find a protein to eat with it!

1 teaspoon lime juice
1 teaspoon rice vinegar or lemon juice
2 teaspoons fresh chopped ginger

1/4 cup chunky nut butter
1/4 cup light coconut milk

Combine the lime juice, vinegar or lemon juice, ginger, nut butter, and coconut milk in a bowl and whisk until smooth.

This can be made ahead. The flavor gets stronger and it gets more spicy after it sits for a day.

Great on cooked chicken! Also delicious for dipping green veggies, cooked or raw. If you put it on veggies, make sure you add some protein!

You need:
1 bowl
1 wire whisk
measuring cups
measuring spoons

Shopping List

lime juice
rice wine vinegar or
lemon juice
fresh ginger
chunky nut butter
light coconut milk

SHARE THIS MEAL WITH FRIENDS AND FAMILY

Ingredients			
lime juice	2 teaspoons	1 tablespoon	4 teaspoons
rice wine vinegar OR	2 teaspoons	1 tablespoon	4 teaspoons
lemon juice	2 teaspoons	1 tablespoon	4 teaspoons
fresh chopped ginger	4 teaspoons	2 tablespoons	8 teaspoons
chunky nut butter	1/2 cup	3/4 cup	1 cup
coconut milk	1/2 cup	3/4 cup	1 cup

SALAD ON THE SIDE

PREP TIME: 5 MINUTES

You need:
bowl
small sharp knife
measuring spoons
measuring cups
blender

Shopping List
cucumbers
lettuce
tomato
snow peas
carrots
lemon juice
extra-light olive oil
fresh or dried mint

2
½ cucumber
½ cup lettuce, red leaf or romaine
½ tomato
12 snow peas
1 teaspoon grated carrot
½ teaspoon lemon juice

3
⅔ teaspoon extra-light olive oil

PLUS!
½ tablespoon fresh or dried mint

EASY! OUCH!

What About Me?

Make sure you add a protein to make this recipe complete!

1 Cut the vegetables into bite–sized pieces and put in a bowl.

2 Whisk together the oil, lemon juice, and mustard. Add any special herbs you like.

3 Pour the dressing over the salad and enjoy!

Nutty Nice Salad Dressing

Put 6 macadamia nuts and 3 tablespoons fresh squeezed lemon or lime juice in a blender. Blend until smooth. Slowly add 1 cup of oil and a few drops of water to make an emulsion. Blend thoroughly and pour onto your salad. For variations use other nuts such as almonds, cashews or pine nuts.

SHARE THIS MEAL WITH FRIENDS AND FAMILY

Ingredients			
cucumbers	1	1½	2
lettuce	1 cup	1½ cups	2 cups
tomatoes	1	1½	2
snow peas	24	36	48
carrots	2 teaspoons	1 tablespoon	4 teaspoons
lemon juice	1 teaspoon	1½ teaspoons	2 teaspoons
extra-light olive oil	1⅓ teaspoons	2 teaspoons	2⅔ teaspoons
fresh or dried mint	1 tablespoon	1½ tablespoons	2 tablespoons

CRUNCHY ALMOND ROLL UP

EASY! OUCH!

PREP TIME: 5 MINUTES

 2 Power Pancakes, about 4" in size, see page 58

 1/8 cup High Power Crunchy Almond Butter, see recipe page 156

 1/2 fresh pear

 1/3 teaspoon slivered almonds

 pinch of cinnamon

 Spread half of the High Power Almond Butter on each pancake. Sprinkle with the cinnamon and slivered almonds.

 Roll up and gently press to hold together.

 Slice the pear. Serve with the almond rolls.

You need:
small knife
measuring cups
measuring spoons

SHARE THIS MEAL WITH FRIENDS AND FAMILY

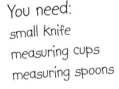

Ingredients	👥	👥	👥👤
pancakes	4	6	8
High Power nut butter	1/4 cup	3/8 cup	1/2 cup
pears	1	1 1/2	2
slivered almonds	2/3 teaspoon	1 teaspoon	1 1/3 teaspoons
cinnamon	2 pinches	3 pinches	4 pinches

CHICKEN KEBOBS

PREP TIME: 15 MINUTES
COOK TIME: 10 MINUTES

You need:
small bowl
small sharp knife
cookie sheet
4 wooden skewers,
about 8"-10" long

Shopping List

chicken breast
red onion
red and green peppers
zucchini
summer squash
cherries
lemon juice
peanut oil
fresh or dried mint

1 2 ounces chicken breast, cut into 1" chunks

2 1/4 cup red onion pieces
1/4 cup sweet red and green pepper pieces
1/4 cup zucchini pieces
1/4 cup summer squash pieces
9 fresh cherries
1/2 tablespoon lemon juice

3 1/2 tablespoon peanut oil

PLUS! 1/2 tablespoon fresh or dried mint

1 Soak the wooden skewers in water while you get the veggies ready. Cut all the ingredients into pieces that are about the same size so that they will cook evenly.

2 Mix the oil, lemon juice, and mint in a bowl. Put the onion, squash and peppers in the bowl. Stir to coat the vegetables.

3 Alternate the chicken pieces with the vegetables on the wooden skewers.

4 Cook on the barbecue or broil in the oven, on a cookie sheet, for about 10 minutes. Turn over and cook for about 10 more minutes or until done.

5 Serve with salad (see recipe, page 80), zucchini chips (see recipe, page 128), and Satay Sauce (see recipe, page 79) for dipping.

SHARE THIS MEAL WITH FRIENDS AND FAMILY

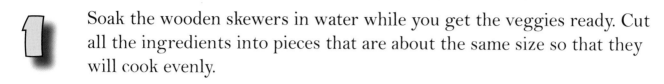

Ingredients			
chicken breast	4 ounces	6 ounces	8 ounces
red onion pieces	½ cup	¾ cup	1 cup
red and green pepper	½ cup	¾ cup	1 cup
zucchini	½ cup	¾ cup	1 cup
summer squash	½ cup	¾ cup	1 cup
cherries	18	27	36
lemon juice	1 tablespoon	1½ tablespoons	2 tablespoons
peanut oil	1 tablespoon	1½ tablespoons	2 tablespoons
mint	1 tablespoon	1½ tablespoons	2 tablespoons

POWER PIZZA CRUST

PREP TIME: 10 MINUTES
COOK TIME: 5 MINUTES

You need:
2 small bowls
spatula
frying pan
measuring cups
measuring spoons

Shopping List
low fat milk
egg whites
oat flour
barley flour
extra-light olive oil
baking powder
salt

 1 cup low fat milk

 2 tablespoons egg whites

 1/3 cup oat flour
3 tablespoons barley flour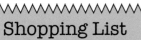

 4 teaspoons extra-light olive oil

 PLUS! 1/2 teaspoon baking powder
pinch salt

❁ *To find barley flour, check a health food store or go on-line (see appendix for web sites). You can use whole wheat flour; but barley is better. It is low glycemic and tastier.*

 Mix the oat flour, barley flour, baking powder and salt and set aside.

 Mix the milk, egg whites and oil in a large bowl. Sprinkle the dry ingredients over the wet and stir together lightly.

 On a warm frying pan pour 2 teaspoons of oil. Pour ⅓ cup batter onto the frying pan to make a 4-5" crust.

 Use the rest of the batter to make the remaining crusts. Pour a few drops of oil onto the pan before each crust.

 Flip when bubbles pop through the crust. Cook until well browned.

 Set on paper towels to cool. (Note—these crusts can be made ahead and saved for later.)

SHARE THIS MEAL WITH FRIENDS AND FAMILY

Ingredients			
low fat milk	2 cups	3 cups	4 cups
egg whites	¼ cup	6 tablespoons	½ cup
oat flour	⅔ cup	1 cup	1⅓ cups
barley flour	6 tablespoons	9 tablespoons	¾ cup
extra-light olive oil	8 teaspoons	¼ cup	16 teaspoons
baking powder	1 teaspoon	1½ teaspoons	2 teaspoons
salt	2 pinches	3 pinches	4 pinches

POWER PIZZA

You need:
small sharp knife
measuring cups
measuring spoons

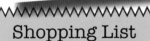
Shopping List

low fat mozzarella cheese
grated parmesan cheese
chicken, turkey, or ham
pasta sauce
extra-light olive oil

 1 ounce shredded low fat mozzarella cheese
1 teaspoon grated parmesan cheese
1 ounce chicken, turkey, or ham

 2 tablespoons pasta sauce (check the index for recommended brands, low in sugar, see food recommendations page 207).

 2/3 teaspoons extra-light olive oil

 Spread the pasta sauce on a pizza crust (see power pizza crust recipe, page 84).

 Cut the chicken, turkey, or ham into small pieces. Place on the sauce.

 Cover with the mozzarella cheese, parmesan cheese and extra-light olive oil.

 Bake in a preheated oven or toaster oven for 5-7 minutes, until the cheese is bubbly and starting to brown.

 Let cool for a few minutes before serving. The cheese can be very hot.

SHARE THIS MEAL WITH FRIENDS AND FAMILY

Ingredients			
low fat mozzarella cheese	2 ounces	3 ounces	4 ounces
parmesan cheese	2 teaspoons	1 tablespoon	4 teaspoons
chicken OR	2 ounces	3 ounces	4 ounces
turkey OR	2 ounces	3 ounces	4 ounces
ham	2 ounces	3 ounces	4 ounces
pasta sauce	1/4 cup	6 tablespoons	1/2 cup
extra-light olive oil	1 1/3 teaspoons	2 teaspoons	2 2/3 teaspoons

SCRAMBLED EGG BOATS

PREP TIME: 10 MINUTES
COOK TIME: 8 MINUTES

You need:
small bowl
spatula
toaster oven or broiler
measuring cups
measuring spoons

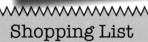

Shopping List

egg whites
shredded cheddar cheese
baking potatoes
pasta sauce
extra-light olive oil

 2 egg whites
1 ounce shredded cheddar cheese

 2 potato skins, see recipe, page 178
1/4 cup pasta sauce

 2/3 teaspoon extra-light olive oil

1 Rub the olive oil on the potato skins. Warm in the broiler or toaster oven for a few minutes until crisp.

2 In a small bowl, whisk the egg whites. In a warm sauté pan heat one tablespoon oil. Add the egg whites. Stir gently with a spatula. Cook the eggs to the consistency you like.

3 Spoon into the potato skins and top with the pasta sauce. Sprinkle the cheese on top of the filled potato skins. Put in the broiler just long enough to melt the cheese.

SHARE THIS MEAL WITH FRIENDS AND FAMILY

Ingredients			
egg whites	4	6	8
shredded cheddar cheese	2 ounces	3 ounces	4 ounces
potato skins	4	6	8
pasta sauce	½ cup	¾ cup	1 cup
extra-light olive oil	1⅓ teaspoons	2 teaspoons	2⅔ teaspoons

TURKEY MELT BOATS

PREP TIME: 8 MINUTES
COOK TIME: 10 MINUTES

You need:
small bowl
small frying pan
toaster oven or broiler
measuring cups
measuring spoons

Shopping List
low fat mozzarella cheese
ground turkey
baking potato
red pizza sauce
extra-light olive oil

 1 ounce low fat mozzarella cheese
1 ounce ground turkey

 2 potato skins, see recipe, page 178
1/4 cup red pizza sauce

 1 teaspoon extra-light olive oil

 Put ⅓ teaspoon extra-light olive oil in a small frying pan. Add the ground turkey and cook until done.

 In a small bowl mix the turkey, red pizza sauce, and cheese.

 Rub the rest of the olive oil on the potato skins. Broil in a toaster oven or broiler for a few minutes to warm.

 Put the turkey, red sauce, and cheese mixture in the potato skins. Put the potato skins in the toaster oven. Broil until the cheese is melted and bubbly.

 Let cool a few minutes before eating, as the cheese can be very hot.

SHARE THIS MEAL WITH FRIENDS AND FAMILY

Ingredients			
low fat mozzarella	2 ounces	3 ounces	4 ounces
ground turkey	2 ounces	3 ounces	4 ounces
potato skins	4	6	8
red pizza sauce	½ cup	¾ cup	1 cup
extra-light olive oil	2 teaspoons	1 tablespoon	4 teaspoons

FLUFFY CHEESE POTATO BOATS

PREP TIME: 8 MINUTES
COOK TIME: 5 MINUTES

You need:
small bowl
small sharp knife
toaster oven or broiler
measuring cups
measuring spoons

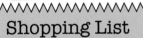

Shopping List

low fat ricotta cheese
egg whites
grated parmesan cheese
baking potatoes
blueberries or raspberries
cantaloupe
extra-light olive oil

1/4 cup low fat ricotta cheese
2 egg whites
1 tablespoon grated parmesan cheese

2 potato skins, see recipe, page 178
1/4 cup blueberries or 1/2 raspberries
1 thin slice cantaloupe, cut crosswise into
two pieces

2/3 teaspoon extra-light olive oil

 Rub the olive oil on the potato skins. In a small bowl, mix the cheese, and egg white until they are well blended. Put half in each potato skin.

 Preheat the broiler or toaster oven. Place the filled potato skins under the broiler or toaster oven until browned, about 3-5 minutes. Watch carefully to avoid burning

 Remove from the heat. Place the melon on top as your sail and the berries as your sailors. Set sail and enjoy.

SHARE THIS MEAL WITH FRIENDS AND FAMILY

Ingredients	👫	👫	👫👤
low fat ricotta cheese	½ cup	1 cup	1½ cups
egg whites	4	6	8
parmesan cheese	⅛ cup	3 tablespoons	¼ cup
potato skins	4	6	8
blueberries	½ cup	¾ cup	1 cup
raspberries	1 cup	1½ cups	2 cups
canteloupe	2 thin slices	3 thin slices	4 thin slices
extra-light olive oil	1⅓ teaspoons	2 teaspoons	2⅔ teaspoons

TURKEY LOG & FRUIT SALAD

You need:
small bowl
small sharp knife
measuring cups
measuring spoons

Shopping List
sliced turkey

string cheese

pears

tangerines

apples

slivered almonds

dried mint

 1 ounce sliced turkey
1 piece string cheese

 1/4 pear, sliced
1/2 tangerine, peeled & sectioned
1/2 apple, cut in bite-sized bits

 2 2/3 teaspoons slivered almonds

PLUS! 1 teaspoon dried mint

 Put the string cheese on the edge of the sliced turkey. Roll it until it looks like a log.

 Cut the fruit in small pieces and mix together in a small bowl.

 Put in a serving bowl and sprinkle with mint and slivered almonds.

SHARE THIS MEAL WITH FRIENDS AND FAMILY

Ingredients	👥	👥	👥👤
sliced turkey	2 ounces	3 ounces	4 ounces
string cheese	2 pieces	3 pieces	4 pieces
pear	½	¾	1
tangerine	1	1½	2
apple	1	1½	2
slivered almonds	5⅓ teaspoons	8 teaspoons	10⅔ teaspoons
dried mint	2 teaspoons	1 tablespoon	4 teaspoons

APPLE MUFFIN MELT

PREP TIME: 5 MINUTES
COOK TIME: 2 MINUTES

You need:
small sharp knife
measuring cups
measuring spoons

Shopping List
low fat shredded cheese
apples
extra-light olive oil
cinnamon

 2 applesauce muffins, see recipe page 176

 1/8 cup low fat shredded cheese

 1/2 apple

 2/3 teaspoon extra-light olive oil

 pinch of cinnamon

EASY! OUCH!

 Slice each muffin in half crosswise to make 4 half muffins.

 In a small bowl mix the oil and the cinnamon.

 Rub oil mixture on each muffin.

 Put in broiler or toaster oven to warm. Take out and cover each with the cheese. Melt in the broiler or toaster oven.

 Slice the apple and serve with the warm muffins.

SHARE THIS MEAL WITH FRIENDS AND FAMILY

Ingredients			
applesauce muffins	4	6	8
shredded cheese	¼ cup	⅜ cup	½ cup
apples	1	1½	2
extra-light olive oil	1⅓ teaspoons	2 teaspoons	2⅔ teaspoons
cinnamon	2 pinches	3 pinches	4 pinches

BROCCOLI BACON SALAD

PREP TIME: 10 MINUTES
COOK TIME: 5 MINUTES

You need:
2 small bowls
small sharp knife
spatula
frying pan
measuring cups
measuring spoons

Shopping List

low fat plain yogurt
turkey bacon
broccoli
carrots
pears
light mayonnaise
walnuts
almonds
black pepper

 2 teaspoons low fat plain yogurt

 6 strips turkey bacon

 2½ cups broccoli
½ cup shredded carrot
½ pear

 2 teaspoons light mayonnaise
1 walnut
1 almond

 Dash black pepper

EASY! OUCH!

 Cook turkey bacon in frying pan. Let cool on paper towels.

 Cut the broccoli into bite-sized pieces and put into a small bowl. Peel and grate the carrot, put into the same bowl. Chop the nuts and add to the salad.

 In another small bowl, mix together yogurt, mayonnaise, and pepper into a sauce.

 Pour the sauce over the salad and stir.

 Crumble the bacon on top. Serve with the pear on the side.

SHARE THIS MEAL WITH FRIENDS AND FAMILY

Ingredients	👥	👥	👥👤
low fat plain yogurt	4 teaspoons	2 tablespoons	8 teaspoons
turkey bacon	12 strips	18 strips	24 strips
broccoli	5 cups	7½ cups	10 cups
carrots	1 cup	1½ cups	2 cups
pears	1	1½	2
light mayonnaise	4 teaspoons	2 tablespoons	8 teaspoons
walnuts	2	3	4
almonds	2	3	4
black pepper	2 dashes	3 dashes	4 dashes

SUMMER CHICKEN SALAD

PREP TIME: 8 MINUTES

You need:
1 small bowl
small sharp knife
measuring cups
measuring spoons
large spoon

Shopping List

low fat plain yogurt
chicken breast
honeydew melon
seedless grapes
cucumber
slivered almonds
extra-light olive oil
dill
lemon juice
salt
pepper

 1 tablespoon low fat plain yogurt

2 ounces cooked chicken breast

 ⅓ cup honeydew melon
⅓ cup seedless grapes
½ cup cucumber

 1⅓ teaspoon slivered almonds
⅓ teaspoon extra-light olive oil

 PLUS!
½ teaspoon dill
1 tablespoon lemon juice
dash salt
dash pepper

 1 Cut the chicken into bite-sized pieces. Put in a small bowl. Add the cucumber and fruit.

 2 Mix the yogurt, olive oil, dill, lemon juice, salt and pepper. Pour over the salad and stir to coat. Sprinkle the slivered almonds on top.

 3 Serve cold.

SHARE THIS MEAL WITH FRIENDS AND FAMILY

Ingredients			
low fat plain yogurt	2 tablespoons	3 tablespoons	¼ cup
chicken breast	4 ounces	6 ounces	8 ounces
honeydew melon	⅔ cup	1 cup	1⅓ cups
seedless grapes	⅔ cup	1 cup	1⅓ cups
cucumber	1 cup	1½ cups	2 cups
slivered almonds	2⅔ teaspoons	4 teaspoons	5⅓ teaspoons
extra-light olive oil	⅔ teaspoon	1 teaspoon	1⅓ teaspoons
dill	1 teaspoon	1½ teaspoons	2 teaspoons
lemon juice	2 tablespoons	3 tablespoons	¼ cup
salt	2 dashes	3 dashes	4 dashes
pepper	2 dashes	3 dashes	4 dashes

HAWAIIAN CHICKEN SALAD

You need:
small bowl
small sharp knife
large spoon
measuring cups
measuring spoons

Shopping List
low fat plain yogurt
chicken breast
celery
pineapple
kiwis
extra-light olive oil
salt
pepper

 1 tablespoon low fat plain yogurt

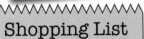 2 ounces cooked chicken breast

 1/4 cup celery
1/2 cup pineapple
1 kiwi

 2/3 teaspoon extra-light olive oil

 PLUS! Dash salt
Dash pepper

 1. Cut the chicken into bite-sized pieces.

 2. Cut the celery and pineapple into small pieces. Peel and cut the kiwi into small pieces.

 3. In a small bowl, mix the olive oil, yogurt, salt and pepper.

 4. Pour the dressing over the fruit and chicken, mixing well.

 5. Serve cold.

SHARE THIS MEAL WITH FRIENDS AND FAMILY

Ingredients			
low fat plain yogurt	2 tablespoons	3 tablespoons	¼ cup
chicken breast	4 ounces	6 ounces	8 ounces
celery	½ cup	¾ cup	1 cup
pineapple	1 cup	1½ cups	2 cups
kiwis	2	3	4
extra-light olive oil	1⅓ teaspoons	2 teaspoons	2⅔ teaspoons
salt	2 dashes	3 dashes	4 dashes
pepper	2 dashes	3 dashes	4 dashes

CREAMY POTATO SOUP

PREP TIME: 6 MINUTES
COOK TIME: 15 MINUTES

You need:
sauté pan
small sharp knife
potato masher
sauce pan
measuring cups
measuring spoons

Shopping List

canned tuna
onions or leeks
kale
thin-skinned potato
light cream
extra-light olive oil
chicken broth
salt
pepper

 1/4 cup canned tuna

 1/4 cup small onion or leek
1 cup kale
1/3 cup thin-skinned potatoes

 1/4 cup light cream
1/3 teaspoon extra-light olive oil

 PLUS! 1 cup chicken broth
pinch salt
pinch pepper

 1 Cut the onion into small pieces. Sauté in the oil on low heat until they are soft and clear.

 2 Cut the kale into thin strips and add to the onion. Cook for 3 more minutes then remove from the heat.

 3 In a saucepan, heat the chicken broth. Cut the potato into cubes. Add to the broth and boil for 6-8 minutes, until soft. Remove from the heat.

 4 Mash the potatoes in the pan. Stir the onion mixture into the soup. Add the cream, onion, salt and pepper.

 5 Add the tuna and mix thoroughly.

 6 Serve warm.

SHARE THIS MEAL WITH FRIENDS AND FAMILY

Ingredients			
canned tuna	½ cup	¾ cup	1 cup
onions or leeks	½ cup	¾ cup	1
kale	2 cups	3 cups	4 cups
potato	⅔ cup	1 cup	1⅓ cups
light cream	½ cup	¾ cup	1 cup
extra-light olive oil	⅔ teaspoon	1 teaspoon	1⅓ teaspoons
chicken broth	2 cups	3 cups	4 cups
salt	2 pinches	3 pinches	4 pinches
pepper	2 pinches	3 pinches	4 pinches

TACOS

You need:
I small bowl
I small sharp knife
I frying pan
measuring cups
measuring spoons

Shopping List
turkey or beef
cheddar cheese
tomatoes
lettuce leaves
taco shells
avocado or guacamole
chili powder
chopped garlic
salt
red pepper

 1/4 cup ground turkey, or beef
1 tablespoon cheddar cheese

 1/2 tomato
2 lettuce leaves
2 taco shells

3 2 tablespoons avocado or guacamole

PLUS! 1 teaspoon chili powder
1/4 teaspoon chopped garlic
1 teaspoon salt
pinch red pepper, to taste

EASY! OUCH! HOT!

 1 Mix the ground meat with the chili powder, chopped garlic, salt, and red pepper. Sauté until browned.

 2 Grate the cheese, slice the tomato, and cut the lettuce into small pieces. Put in a bowl and mix.

 3 Spread the avocado or guacamole into the taco shell.

 4 Layer the rest of the ingredients in the shell—meat, tomato, lettuce then cheese.

SHARE THIS MEAL WITH FRIENDS AND FAMILY

Ingredients			
turkey or beef	½ cup	¾ cup	1 cup
cheddar cheese	2 tablespoons	3 tablespoons	¼ cup
tomatoes	1	1½	2
lettuce leaves	4 leaves	6 leaves	8 leaves
taco shells	4 shells	6 shells	8 shells
avocado or guacamole	¼ cup	6 tablespoons	½ cup
chili powder	2 teaspoons	1 tablespoon	4 teaspoons
chopped garlic	½ teaspoon	¾ teaspoon	1 teaspoon
salt	2 teaspoons	1 tablespoon	4 teaspoons
red pepper	2 pinches	3 pinches	4 pinches

CHILI

You need:
1 small sharp knife
1 spatula
1 frying pan
1 sauce pan
measuring cups
measuring spoons

Shopping List
ground beef or turkey
grated cheddar cheese
black beans
canned tomatoes
onions
extra-light olive oil
chili powder
chopped garlic
salt
red pepper

 ¼ cup lean ground beef or turkey
⅛ cup grated cheddar cheese

 ⅓ cup canned (or soaked) black beans
¾ cup canned tomatoes, liquid drained
¼ onion

 ⅔ teaspoon extra-light olive oil

 ½ tablespoon chili powder
½ teaspoon chopped garlic
½ teaspoon salt
pinch red pepper, to taste

EASY! OUCH! HOT!

 Chop the onion and sauté gently in the olive oil, until onions are wilted. Take care not to brown them, or they will not be as sweet.

 Cook the meat thoroughly, then add all remaining ingredients except the cheese.

 Cook on low heat for 10-15 minutes. Serve with cheese on top.

 Note: Chili can be made in advance to let the flavors blend. It will get spicier if it sits in the refrigerator overnight!

SHARE THIS MEAL WITH FRIENDS AND FAMILY

Ingredients			
ground turkey or beef	½ cup	¾ cup	1 cup
cheddar cheese	¼ cup	⅜ cup	½ cup
black beans	⅔ cup	1 cup	1⅓ cups
canned tomatoes	1½ cups	2¼ cups	3 cups
onions	½ onion	¾ onion	1 onion
extra-light olive oil	1⅓ teaspoons	2 teaspoons	2⅔ teaspoons
chili powder	1 tablespoon	1½ tablespoons	2 tablespoons
chopped garlic	1 teaspoon	1½ teaspoons	2 teaspoons
salt	1 teaspoon	1½ teaspoons	2 teaspoons
red pepper	2 pinches	3 pinches	4 pinches

MIGHTY NICE POTATO CAKES

PREP TIME: 15 MINUTES
COOK TIME: 15 MINUTES

You need:
small bowl
spatula
frying pan
measuring cups
measuring spoons

Shopping List

whey protein powder
egg whites
potatoes
applesauce
light sour cream
extra-light olive oil
salt
pepper

 1/8 cup whey protein powder
1/4 cup egg whites

 1/4 cup cooked potato ✿
1/3 cup applesauce

 1 tablespoon light sour cream
1/3 teaspoon extra-light olive oil

 PLUS! Pinch salt
Pinch pepper

 Put the potato in a small bowl. Mix together with the whey protein powder, egg whites, salt, and pepper.

 Heat 1 teaspoon olive oil in a sauté pan. Drop spoonfuls of the potato mixture in the pan and flatten with a spatula to make a pancake shape.

 Cook until brown, then flip to the other side. It takes about 5 minutes per side. Continue for the rest of the batter.

 Serve warm and top with the sour cream.

 Serve the applesauce on the side.

SHARE THIS MEAL WITH FRIENDS AND FAMILY

Ingredients			
whey protein powder	1/4 cup	3/8 cup	1/2 cup
egg whites	1/2 cup	3/4 cup	1 cup
potatoes	1/2 cup	3/4 cup	1 cup
applesauce	2/3 cup	1 cup	1 1/3 cups
light sour cream	2 tablespoons	3 tablespoons	1/4 cup
extra-light olive oil	2/3 teaspoon	1 teaspoon	1 1/3 teaspoons
salt	2 pinches	3 pinches	4 pinches
pepper	2 pinches	3 pinches	4 pinches

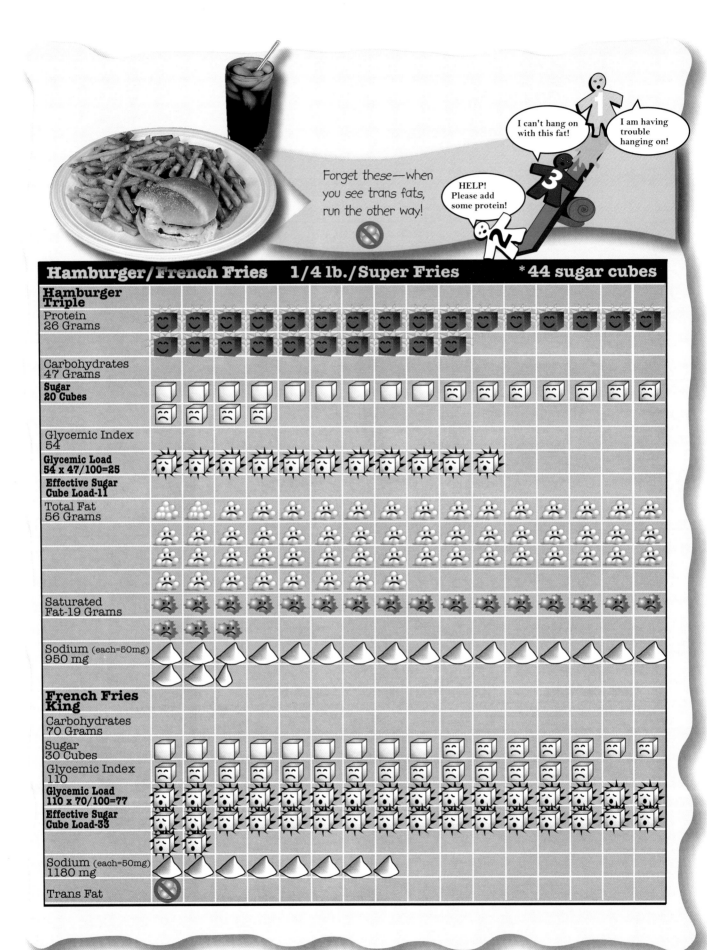

Forget these—when you see trans fats, run the other way!

I can't hang on with this fat!

I am having trouble hanging on!

HELP! Please add some protein!

Hamburger/French Fries	1/4 lb./Super Fries	*44 sugar cubes

Hamburger Triple

Protein 26 Grams

Carbohydrates 47 Grams

Sugar 20 Cubes

Glycemic Index 54

Glycemic Load 54 x 47/100=25

Effective Sugar Cube Load-11

Total Fat 56 Grams

Saturated Fat-19 Grams

Sodium (each=50mg) 950 mg

French Fries King

Carbohydrates 70 Grams

Sugar 30 Cubes

Glycemic Index 110

Glycemic Load 110 x 70/100=77

Effective Sugar Cube Load-33

Sodium (each=50mg) 1180 mg

Trans Fat

"TYPICAL AMERICAN MEAL??!!"

All around the world a hamburger, french fries, and a cola drink are considered the typical American meal. It is shocking to travel into Asian countries and find a fast food hamburger restaurant. The sad part is that the "typical American meal" is a significant contributor to the alarming increase of childhood obesity, childhood Type II diabetes, and chronic behavioral problems. It is not only the amount of sugar in the so-called meal, (113 sugar cubes), it is the trans fat, the caffeine, the preservatives and the artificial flavors that are so detrimental to our health. The fast food companies entice children with toys and playgrounds yet have little concern for their health.

Help! I don't like the way caffeine feels

Help! The sugar and the caffeine make me feel jittery!

Cola	X-Large 44 ounces	*58 sugar cubes
Carbohydrates 147 Grams		
Sugar 64 Cubes		
Glycemic Index 90		
Glycemic Load 90 x 147/100=132		
Effective Sugar Cube Load-58		
Caffeine 136 mg		

DID YOU KNOW?

- In many states the highway patrol carries 2 gallons of cola in the trunk to remove blood from the highway after a car accident.
- You can put a T-bone steak in a bowl of cola and it will be gone in two days.
- To clean a toilet: pour a can of cola into the toilet bowl and let the "real thing" sit for one hour, then flush clean. The citric acid in cola removes stain from vitreous china.
- To remove rust spots from chrome car bumpers: rub the bumper with rumpled-up pieces of aluminum foil dipped in cola.
- To clean corrosion from car battery terminals: pour a can of cola over the terminals to bubble away the corrosion.
- To loosen a rusted bolt: apply a cloth soaked in cola to the rusted bolt for several minutes.
- To remove grease from clothes: empty a can of cola into a load of greasy clothes, add detergent, and run through a regular cycle. The cola will help loosen grease stains. It will also clean road stains from your windshield.

For your info:

- The active ingredient in cola is phosphoric acid. It will dissolve a nail in about 4 days. Phosphoric acid also leaches calcium from bones and is a major contributor to the rising increase in osteoporosis.
- To carry cola syrup (the concentrate) the commercial truck must use the "hazardous material" place cards reserved for highly corrosive materials.
- The distributors of cola have been using it to clean the engines of their trucks for about 20 years!

Caffeine:

- The active ingredient in caffeine is DARPP-32. It is associated with causing an increased risk of schizophrenia.
- Small doses of caffeine can cause stiffening of the blood vessel walls, increase in blood pressure, and stiffness of the aorta.
- Caffeine is an addictive substance. When you try to quit you get a severe headache that can last for about 24 hours.
- Caffeine increases alertness, reduces fine motor coordination, alters sleep patterns, and causes headaches, nervousness and dizziness.

YUK!

Help! I don't like the way caffeine feels

RICE AND BEANS—PERFECT PROTEIN???

Vegetarianism is a wonderful dietary program if adequate protein is a component of every meal. Unfortunately there are many falsehoods in the dietary information that is available to the public and one is that beans and rice are a perfect protein. Research, such as the glycemic index, shows that the combination of beans and rice is predominately a carbohydrate.

One serving of rice and beans equals **18 grams** of protein and **82 grams** of carbohydrate. The Nature's Mighty Bites™ have taught us that a balanced meal is a ratio of **one** unit (7 grams) of protein to **one** unit (9 grams) of carbohydrate. However rice and beans equal 2½ units of protein and 9 units of carbohydrate. To make this a complete meal you need to add **7½ units** of protein. If you are vegetarian that is a lot of tofu or meat substitute.

You will be amazed, if you start eating protein first, to see that the amount of carbohydrate needed to feel satisfied will be much less.

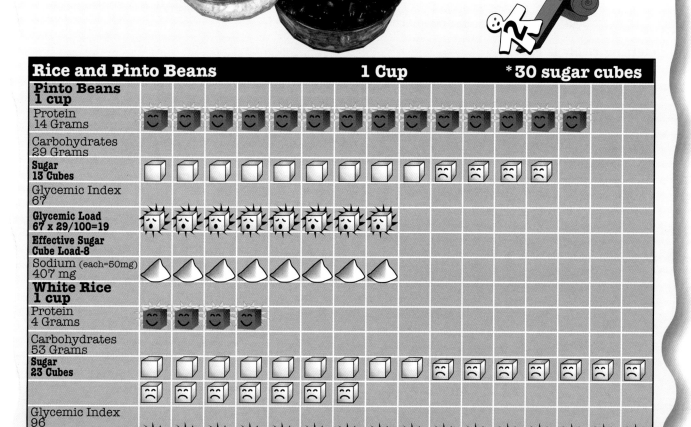

Rice and Pinto Beans		1 Cup	*30 sugar cubes

Pinto Beans 1 cup
- Protein 14 Grams
- Carbohydrates 29 Grams
- Sugar 13 Cubes
- Glycemic Index 67
- Glycemic Load 67 x 29/100=19
- Effective Sugar Cube Load-8
- Sodium (each=50mg) 407 mg

White Rice 1 cup
- Protein 4 Grams
- Carbohydrates 53 Grams
- Sugar 23 Cubes
- Glycemic Index 96
- Glycemic Load 96 x 53/100=51
- Effective Sugar Cube Load-22

Dinner

Dinner is a very important time to share stories, provide support, and set family goals. Everyone can join in preparing the evening meal by choosing special flavors and foods to make together. Enjoy the special recipes!

Creative Dinner Ideas:

- Set the dinner table in a **special** way. Put fun, **creative** place mats, colorful napkins and **candles**. The children can color white paper place mats with creative pictures—one for each day of the week.

- Make dinner time a **fun** time for all. This is a time when a family can take time to share with each other the **positive events** of the day. No time at the table for negative events or negative talk!

- Take turns setting and clearing the table. You can even pretend that you are at a very special **restaurant** and each member of the family can have a different role. One can be the maître d', one the head waiter, and one the chef. Remember, your "guests" are very special people!

Getting ready is easy:

- Plan the menus on the weekend so you can go shopping and have the necessary ingredients.

- Have weekend "think tanks" to plan new and exciting ideas.

- Look in magazines to get decorating and serving ideas.

- Plan special desserts and make them on the weekend so you have plenty of time to spend with the family in the evening.

- Use leftovers for lunch the next day.

MIGHTY TASTY MARINADE

PREP TIME: 5 MINUTES
MARINATE TIME: 1 HOUR

Check with Me!

EASY!

You need:
medium bowl
measuring spoons

Choose the protein you want to marinade. This makes a double serving so make sure you double your protein amount. For example, a 4 ounce flank steak or a 4 ounce chicken breast.

1 teaspoon fructose

1 tablespoon extra-light olive oil

PLUS!
2 tablespoons brown mustard
1 tablespoon low salt tamari
1 teaspoon chopped garlic

1. Blend the fructose, mustard, tamari, garlic, and olive oil in a medium sized bowl.

2. Add the protein and stir to coat. Cover and let marinate in the refrigerator for at least an hour or up to a day.

3. As you cook your protein, spoon the extra marinade over the protein.

Shopping List
fructose
extra-light olive oil
brown mustard
low salt tamari
chopped garlic

SHARE THIS MEAL WITH FRIENDS AND FAMILY

Ingredients	👫	👫	👫👫
fructose	2 teaspoons	1 tablespoon	4 teaspoons
extra-light olive oil	2 tablespoons	3 tablespoons	1/4 cup
brown mustard	1/4 cup	6 tablespoons	1/2 cup
low salt tamari	1/8 cup	3 tablespoons	1/4 cup
chopped garlic	2 teaspoons	1 tablespoon	4 teaspoons

MANDARIN MARINADE STEAK

PREP TIME: 1 HOUR

COOK TIME: 3-5 MINUTES

You need:
medium bowl
small sharp knife
spatula
broiler pan
measuring cups
measuring spoons

Shopping List
flank steak/lean cut beef
fructose
kiwis
grapes
extra-light olive oil
fresh mint
chopped garlic
brown mustard
low salt tamari

 2 ounces flank steak or other lean cut beef

 1/2 teaspoon fructose
3/4 kiwi
1/3 cup grapes

 2/3 teaspoon extra-light olive oil

PLUS! 1 teaspoon fresh mint
1 teaspoon chopped garlic
1 tablespoon brown mustard
1/2 tablespoon low salt tamari

 Blend the fructose, mustard, low salt tamari, garlic, and oil in a medium-sized bowl.

 Add the beef and stir to coat. Cover and let marinate in the refrigerator for at least an hour, or overnight.

 Pre-heat the broiler. Place the steak on a broiler pan and cook for 4-5 minutes. Remove from the oven and carefully flip the steak.

 Spoon the extra marinade over the steak. Broil for 3-5 minutes more, if you like it well done.

 Cut the fruit into bite-sized pieces. Stir gently and serve.

SHARE THIS MEAL WITH FRIENDS AND FAMILY

Ingredients			
flank steak or lean beef	4 ounces	6 ounces	8 ounces
fructose	1 teaspoon	1½ teaspoons	2 teaspoons
kiwis	1½	2¼	3
grapes	⅔ cup	1 cup	1⅓ cups
extra-light olive oil	1⅓ teaspoons	2 teaspoons	2⅔ teaspoons
fresh mint	2 teaspoons	1 tablespoon	4 teaspoons
chopped garlic	2 teaspoons	1 tablespoon	4 teaspoons
brown mustard	⅛ cup	3 tablespoons	¼ cup
low salt tamari	1 tablespoon	1½ tablespoons	⅛ cup

GLAZED CHICKEN

PREP TIME: 5 MINUTES
MARINATE TIME: 1 HOUR
COOK TIME: 35 MINUTES

You need:
small bowl
small sharp knife
spatula
sauce pan
baking pan
measuring cups
measuring spoons

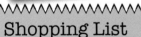

Shopping List
chicken breast
apple juice
fructose
broccoli
kiwis
pineapple chunks
extra-light olive oil
brown mustard
low salt tamari
chopped garlic

2 ounces chicken breast

¹/₃ cup apple juice
¹/₂ teaspoon fructose

1 cup broccoli
¹/₂ kiwi
3 pineapple chunks

²/₃ teaspoon extra-light olive oil

PLUS!
1 tablespoon brown mustard
¹/₄ tablespoon low salt tamari
1 teaspoon chopped garlic

EASY! OUCH! HOT!

 1 Blend fructose, oil, mustard, low salt tamari, garlic, and apple juice in a small bowl.

 2 Add the chicken and stir to coat completely. Cover and let the chicken marinate in the refrigerator for at least one hour, or overnight.

 3 Preheat the oven to 350°. Put the chicken in a baking pan and bake for 35-40 minutes. Poke the chicken with a fork. If the juice is red, it needs more baking time. If the juice is clear it is done.

 4 In a sauce pan put about 2 inches of water and bring to a boil. Put the broccoli in and cover, cooking for 3-4 minutes. When cooked to your preferred style, pour into a strainer to pour out the excess water.

 5 Peel and slice the kiwi and serve with the pineapple chunks on the side.

SHARE THIS MEAL WITH FRIENDS AND FAMILY

Ingredients			
chicken breast	4 ounces	6 ounces	8 ounces
apple juice	2/3 cup	1 cup	1 1/3 cups
fructose	1 teaspoon	1 1/2 teaspoons	2 teaspoons
broccoli	2 cups	3 cups	4 cups
kiwis	1	1 1/2	2
pineapple chunks	6	9	12
extra-light olive oil	1 1/3 teaspoons	2 teaspoons	2 2/3 teaspoons
brown mustard	1/8 cup	3 tablespoons	1/4 cup
low salt tamari	1/2 tablespoon	3/4 tablespoon	1 tablespoon
chopped garlic	2 teaspoons	1 tablespoon	4 teaspoons

LEMON SALMON STEAK

PREP TIME: 1 HOUR
COOK TIME: 15 MINUTES

You need:
1 medium bowl
small sharp knife
spatula
broiler
measuring cups
measuring spoons

Shopping List

salmon steaks
snow peas
extra-light olive oil
limes
red hot chili peppers
basil
coriander
mint

 3 ounces salmon steak

 1 cup snow peas
mixed green salad (see recipe, page 80)

 2/3 teaspoon extra-light olive oil

PLUS! juice of 2 limes
2 red hot chili peppers
1/2 teaspoon basil
1/2 teaspoon coriander
1/2 teaspoon mint

EASY! OUCH! HOT!

 Slice the red hot chili peppers, remove the seeds, and chop into small pieces. Wash your hands, the juice can sting! Squeeze the limes and add the juice to the pepper pieces. Add the basil, coriander, and mint. Put the salmon in a bowl. Pour the mixture over the salmon, and let marinate for one or more hours.

 Preheat the broiler or toaster oven. Place the salmon steak on the broiler pan.

 Broil for 5-7 minutes. The salmon should start to brown. Remove from the oven and flip over. Pour more marinade on the salmon. Broil for 3-5 more minutes until browned and cooked.

 Cut the snow peas into 1 inch pieces. Add to the salad.

 Put the salmon steak on top of the salad, spooning the extra marinade from the pan onto the salad.

SHARE THIS MEAL WITH FRIENDS AND FAMILY

Ingredients			
salmon steaks	6 ounces	9 ounces	12 ounces
snow peas	2 cups	3 cups	4 cups
green salads	2	3	4
extra-light olive oil	1⅓ teaspoons	2 teaspoons	2⅔ teaspoons
limes	4	6	8
red hot chili peppers	4	6	8
basil	1 teaspoon	1½ teaspoons	2 teaspoons
coriander	1 teaspoon	1½ teaspoons	2 teaspoons
mint	1 teaspoon	1½ teaspoons	2 teaspoons

SPICY ORANGE SALAD

You need:
3 small bowls
small sharp knife
spatula
baking dish
measuring cups
measuring spoons

Shopping List
extra-firm tofu
mandarin orange
small carrots
cucumbers
lime
extra-light olive oil
salt
black pepper
fructose
red pepper
fresh or dried mint

 ½ cup extra-firm tofu

 ½ cup mandarin orange slices
2 small carrots
½ cucumber
wedge of lime

 ⅔ teaspoon extra-light olive oil

 PLUS!
pinch of salt
pinch of black pepper
pinch of fructose
pinch of red pepper
1 tablespoon fresh mint or 1 teaspoon dried

 Peel and grate the cucumber and carrots. Put in a small bowl.

 Stir in the orange slices.

 Cut the tofu into bite-sized pieces and add to the same bowl.

 In another small bowl, mix together the salt, pepper, fructose, red pepper, fresh mint, olive oil, and lime juice.

 Add the mixture to the tofu and vegetables. Serve.

SHARE THIS MEAL WITH FRIENDS AND FAMILY

Ingredients	👥	👥	👥👥
extra-firm tofu	1 cup	1½ cups	2 cups
mandarin orange	1 cup	1½ cups	2 cups
small carrots	4	6	8
cucumbers	1	1½	2
wedge of lime	2 wedges	3 wedges	4 wedges
extra-light olive oil	1⅓ teaspoons	2 teaspoons	2⅔ teaspoons
salt	2 pinches	3 pinches	4 pinches
black pepper	2 pinches	3 pinches	4 pinches
fructose	2 pinches	3 pinches	4 pinches
red pepper	2 pinches	3 pinches	4 pinches
fresh mint OR	⅛ cup	3 tablespoons	¼ cup
dried mint	2 teaspoons	1 tablespoon	4 teaspoons

MIGHTY MAC & CHEESE

PREP TIME: 5 MINUTES
COOK TIME: 10 MINUTES
BAKE TIME: 40 MINUTES

You need:
sauce pan
strainer
baking dish
mixing spoon
measuring cups
measuring spoons

Shopping List
low fat milk
shredded cheddar cheese
shredded mozzarella cheese
elbow macaroni
butter
salt
pepper
Dijon mustard

 1 cup low fat milk

 1/2 cup shredded cheddar cheese
1/4 cup shredded mozzarella cheese

 1/2 cup elbow macaroni

 1/4 stick butter

 1/4 teaspoon salt
1/8 teaspoon pepper
3/4 teaspoon Dijon mustard

1 Boil 3 cups pure water. Add the macaroni and boil for 9-10 minutes. Do not let it get mushy. Drain and set aside.

2 Melt the butter in a saucepan. Add the salt, pepper and stir until well mixed. Add the mustard.

3 Take the pan off the heat and slowly stir in the milk. Put the saucepan back on the heat and bring to a boil. Boil and stir for one minute.

4 Add the cheese to the sauce mixture. Stir until the cheese is melted.

5 Add the macaroni and mix thoroughly.

TIP *To bake your macaroni, preheat the oven to 350°. Put extra-light olive oil around a quart baking dish. Add the macaroni and cheese. Bake until the sauce in the center is firm, about 40 minutes.*

SHARE THIS MEAL WITH FRIENDS AND FAMILY

Ingredients			
low fat milk	2 cups	3 cups	4 cups
cheddar cheese	1 cup	1½ cups	2 cups
mozzarella cheese	½ cup	¾ cup	1 cup
elbow macaroni	1 cup	1½ cups	2 cups
butter	½ stick	¾ stick	1 stick
salt	½ teaspoon	¾ teaspoon	1 teaspoon
pepper	¼ teaspoon	⅜ teaspoon	½ teaspoon
Dijon mustard	1½ teaspoons	2¼ teaspoons	3 teaspoons

ZUCCHINI CHIPS

PREP TIME: 10 MINUTES
COOK TIME: 1-2 MINUTES

You need:
2 small bowls
small sharp knife
wire whisk
frying pan
measuring cups
measuring spoons
mandoline/slicer

Shopping List
egg whites
zucchini
garbanzo/lentil flour
peanut oil
McCormick's lemon herb
seasoning

 1 4 egg whites, lightly beaten

 2 1 zucchini
¼ cup garbanzo bean or lentil flour

 3 1 cup peanut oil

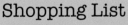 **PLUS!** McCormick's lemon herb seasoning, to taste

 **TIP** *If you slice the zucchini into long, very thin strips you can make shoestring zucchini fries.*

Great addition for other recipes, or a party treat

EASY! OUCH! HOT!

 1 Pour the oil into a deep frying pan on medium heat. It should gently bubble when the oil is hot.

 2 Cut the zucchini into very thin circles. If you use a mandoline or food processor, you can slice the zucchini into very thin chips.

 3 Put the egg whites in a bowl. Pour over the vegetables and gently toss to coat evenly.

 4 Put the flour into a shallow bowl. Add the McCormick's seasoning and mix well. Gently turn the squash pieces in the flour mixture until they are coated.

 5 Carefully set the zucchini into the oil. Fry briefly, about a minute. Lift out with a slotted spoon and set on paper towels to cool and drain.

 6 You have now created your own healthy home made zucchini chips!

SHARE THIS MEAL WITH FRIENDS AND FAMILY

Ingredients	👥	👥	👥👥
egg whites	8	12	16
zucchini	2	3	4
garbanzo/lentil flour	½ cup	¾ cup	1 cup
peanut oil	2 cups	3 cups	4 cups
McCormick's seasoning	2 shakes	3 shakes	4 shakes

 A mandoline is very sharp, so be very careful. If children are helping, use a food processor that slices. It is much safer.

SALMON SAUCERS

You need:
small knife
measuring spoons

Shopping List
smoked salmon
cucumbers
carrots
light cream cheese
lemon
dried dill

 2 power pancakes, about 4" across. See recipe, page 58

 1 1/2 ounce smoked salmon

 1/2 cucumber
1 carrot

 1 tablespoon light cream cheese

PLUS! 1 slice lemon
pinch dried dill

1 Stir the cream cheese to make creamy.

2 Spread onto one pancake, sprinkle with dill and lemon.

3 Put the salmon on top of the cream cheese and top with second pancake to make the saucer.

4 Cut the cucumber and carrots into sticks. Serve on the side.

SHARE THIS MEAL WITH FRIENDS AND FAMILY

Ingredients			
pancakes	4	6	8
smoked salmon	3 ounces	4½ ounces	6 ounces
cucumbers	1	1½	2
carrots	2	3	4
light cream cheese	⅛ cup	3 tablespoons	¼ cup
lemon	2 slices	3 slices	4 slices
dried dill	2 pinches	3 pinches	4 pinches

EGG SALAD SAUCERS

PREP TIME: 5 MINUTES
COOK TIME: 5 MINUTES

You need:
small bowl
spatula
sauté pan
measuring cups
measuring spoons

Shopping List
egg whites
celery
spinach leaves
hummus
extra-light olive oil
black pepper

 2 power pancakes, about 4" across. See recipe, page 58

 ¼ cup egg whites

 ⅛ cup chopped celery
3 or 4 spinach leaves, finely chopped
2 tablespoons hummus

 ⅔ teaspoon extra-light olive oil

 pinch black pepper

 In a sauté pan, warm the olive oil. Add the egg whites and cook to your desired consistency.

 Remove from the heat and break the egg whites into pieces.

 In a small bowl, mix together the egg white, hummus, celery, chopped spinach leaves, and olive oil.

 Spread the egg salad onto one pancake. Top with the second pancake.

SHARE THIS MEAL WITH FRIENDS AND FAMILY

Ingredients	👫	👫	👫👤
pancakes	4	6	8
egg whites	½ cup	¾ cup	1 cup
chopped celery	¼ cup	⅜ cup	½ cup
spinach leaves	6	9	12
hummus	¼ cup	6 tablespoons	½ cup
extra-light olive oil	1⅓ teaspoon	2 teaspoons	2⅔ teaspoons
black pepper	2 pinches	3 pinches	4 pinches

TROPICAL CHICKEN

PREP TIME: 8 MINUTES
COOK TIME: 5 MINUTES

You need:
small bowl
small sharp knife
sauté pan
measuring cups
measuring spoons

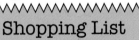

Shopping List
chicken
fresh spinach
celery *lime*
carrots
bean sprouts
snow peas
mandarin orange
macadamia nuts
extra-light olive oil

 2 ounces cooked chicken

1/2 cup fresh spinach
1/2 cup chopped celery
2 tablespoons carrots, finely chopped
1 tablespoon bean sprouts
6 snow peas
1/3 cup mandarin orange slices

1 macadamia nut, chopped
1/3 teaspoon extra-light olive oil

 Put the oil on the sauté pan. Add the cut chicken and vegetables and sauté on medium heat until cooked.

 In a separate bowl, mix the olive oil, lime, salt and pepper. Pour over the chicken and vegetables.

 Serve the mandarin orange on the side.

SHARE THIS MEAL WITH FRIENDS AND FAMILY

Ingredients			
chicken	4 ounces	6 ounces	8 ounces
fresh spinach	1 cup	1½ cups	2 cups
chopped celery	1 cup	1½ cups	2 cups
chopped carrots	¼ cup	6 tablespoons	½ cup
bean sprouts	2 tablespoons	¼ cup	6 tablespoons
snow peas	12	18	24
mandarin orange slices	⅔ cup	1 cup	1⅓ cup
macadamia nuts	2	3	4
extra-light olive oil	⅔ teaspoon	1 teaspoon	1⅓ teaspoons

MIGHTY NUTTY CHICKEN

You need:
small bowl
small sharp knife
frying pan
measuring cups
measuring spoon
coffee grinder
plastic bag

Shopping List

chicken breast
egg whites
snow peas
celery
plums
extra-light olive oil
nuts
salt
black pepper

 2 ounces skinless chicken breast
1 egg white

 1 cup snow peas
8-10 celery sticks
1 plum

 1/4 cup extra-light olive oil
1/4 cup ground nuts

PLUS! pinch of salt
pinch of black pepper
2 tablespoons cold water

 Heat the olive oil in a small frying pan. Cut the chicken into bite-size pieces. Pour the egg white in a small bowl. Roll the chicken in the egg white to cover evenly.

 Put the nuts in a coffee grinder to make a nutty flour. In a small plastic bag, combine the nuts, salt, and pepper. Add the chicken and gently roll to coat with the nut mixture.

 Put the chicken in the frying pan, cooking for 3-4 minutes on each side.

 When the chicken is cooked through, remove from the pan. Put on a paper towel to cool slightly.

 Serve with the snow peas, celery, and fruit.

 *If you are allergic to nuts, use oat or barley flour. Use the same quantity as the ground nuts. If you are vegetarian, substitute tofu for the chicken.*

SHARE THIS MEAL WITH FRIENDS AND FAMILY

Ingredients			
chicken breast	4 ounces	6 ounces	8 ounces
egg whites	2	3	4
snow peas	2 cups	3 cups	4 cups
celery sticks	16	24	32
plums	2	3	4
extra-light olive oil	½ cup	¾ cup	1 cup
ground nuts	½ cup	¾ cup	1 cup
salt	2 pinches	3 pinches	4 pinches
black pepper	2 pinches	3 pinches	4 pinches
cold water	¼ cup	6 tablespoons	½ cup

MIGHTY NUTTY FISH STICKS

PREP TIME: 10 MINUTES
COOK TIME: 6 MINUTESS

You need:
small bowl
small sharp knife
frying pan
measuring cups
measuring spoons
coffee grinder
plastic bag

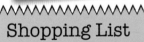

Shopping List
fish
egg whites
snow peas
celery
pear
extra-light olive oil
nuts
salt
black pepper

 1 — 2 ounces fish
1 egg white

 **2** — 1 cup snow peas
8-10 celery sticks
1/2 pear

3 — 1/4 cup extra-light olive oil
1/4 cup ground nuts

 PLUS! — pinch of salt
pinch of black pepper

EASY! OUCH! HOT!

 Cut the fish into bite-size pieces. Pour the egg white in a small bowl. Roll the fish in the egg white to cover each piece evenly.

 Put the nuts in a coffee grinder to make a nutty flour. In a small plastic bag, combine the nuts, salt, and pepper. Add the fish and gently roll to coat with the nut mixture.

 Heat the olive oil in a small frying pan. Add the fish, cooking for 3-4 minutes on each side.

 When the fish is cooked through, remove from the pan. Put on a paper towel to cool slightly.

 Serve with the snow peas, celery and the fruit.

 *If you are allergic to nuts, use oat or barley flour. Use the same quantity as the ground nuts.*

SHARE THIS MEAL WITH FRIENDS AND FAMILY

Ingredients	👥	👥	👥👤
fish	4 ounces	6 ounces	8 ounces
egg whites	2	3	4
snow peas	2 cups	3 cups	4 cups
celery sticks	16	24	32
pears	1	1½	2
extra-light olive oil	½ cup	¾ cup	1 cup
ground nuts	½ cup	¾ cup	1 cup
salt	2 pinches	3 pinches	4 pinches
black pepper	2 pinches	3 pinches	4 pinches

COCONUT CRUNCH CHICKEN

You need:
small bowl
small sharp knife
frying pan
measuring cups
measuring spoons
plastic bag

Shopping List
chicken breast
egg whites
peaches
pineapple
unsweetened coconut
extra-light olive oil
salt
red pepper
lime

 2 ounces skinless chicken breast
1 egg white

 1 peach
1/2 cup pineapple

 2 tablespoons shredded unsweetened coconut
1/4 cup extra-light olive oil

 PLUS! pinch of salt
pinch of red pepper
wedge of lime

 Heat the olive oil in a small frying pan.

 Cut the chicken into bite-size pieces. In a small bowl, roll the chicken in the egg white to cover evenly. In a plastic bag, combine the coconut, salt and pepper.

 Add the chicken and gently coat with the mixture. Put the chicken in the frying pan, cooking for 3-4 minutes on each side.

 When the chicken is cooked through, remove from the pan. Put on a paper towel to cool slightly.

 Serve with the fruit. Squeeze the wedge of lime over everything.

 *If you are vegetarian, substitute tofu for the chicken.*

SHARE THIS MEAL WITH FRIENDS AND FAMILY

Ingredients	👥	👥	👥👤
chicken breast	4 ounces	6 ounces	8 ounces
egg whites	2	3	4
peaches	2	3	4
pineapple	1 cup	1½ cups	2 cups
unsweetened coconut	¼ cup	6 tablespoons	½ cup
extra-light olive oil	½ cup	¾ cup	1 cup
salt	2 pinches	3 pinches	4 pinches
red pepper	2 pinches	3 pinches	4 pinches
lime	2 wedges	3 wedges	4 wedges

COCONUT CRUNCH SHRIMP

PREP TIME: 10 MINUTES
COOK TIME: 3 MINUTES

You need:
small bowl
small sharp knife
frying pan
measuring cups
measuring spoons
plastic bag

Shopping List

shrimp
egg whites
peach
pineapple
unsweetened coconut
extra-light olive oil
salt
red pepper
lime

 2 ounces shrimp
1 egg white

 1 peach
1/2 cup pineapple

 2 tablespoons shredded unsweetened coconut
1/4 cup extra-light olive oil

 PLUS! pinch of salt
pinch of red pepper
wedge of lime

 1 Heat the olive oil in a small frying pan.

 2 In a small bowl, roll the shrimp in the egg white to cover evenly. In a small plastic bag, combine the coconut, salt and pepper.

 3 Add the shrimp and gently coat with the mixture. Add the shrimp to the frying pan, cooking for 1-2 minutes on each side.

 4 When the shrimp is cooked through, remove from the pan. Put on a paper towel to cool slightly.

 5 Cut the peach into slices. Serve with the shrimp. Squeeze the wedge of lime over everything.

 *If you are vegetarian, substitute tofu for the chicken.*

SHARE THIS MEAL WITH FRIENDS AND FAMILY

Ingredients	👥	👥	👥👤
shrimp	4 ounces	6 ounces	8 ounces
egg whites	2	3	4
peaches	2	3	4
pineapple	1 cup	1½ cups	2 cups
shredded coconut	¼ cup	6 tablespoons	½ cup
extra-light olive oil	½ cup	¾ cup	1 cup
salt	2 pinches	3 pinches	4 pinches
red pepper	2 pinches	3 pinches	4 pinches
lime	2 wedges	3 wedges	4 wedges

CHICKEN & CORN FRITTERS

PREP TIME: 8 MINUTES
COOK TIME: 8 MINUTES

You need:
- small plastic bag
- small sharp knife
- spatula
- frying pan
- measuring cups
- measuring spoons

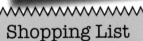

Shopping List
- chicken breast
- egg white
- corn meal
- cucumber
- strawberries
- extra-light olive oil
- salt
- red pepper
- black pepper
- lemon

 2 ounces skinless chicken breast
1 egg white

 ⅛ cup corn meal
¼ cucumber
1 cup strawberries

 ¼ cup extra-light olive oil

PLUS! dash of salt
dash of red pepper
dash of black pepper
wedge of lemon

 Heat the olive oil in a small frying pan. Cut the chicken into bite-size pieces.

 In a small plastic bag, mix the corn meal, salt, and red and black pepper. Add the chicken to coat with the corn meal mixture.

 Add the coated chicken to the frying pan, cooking for 3-4 minutes on each side.

 When the chicken is thoroughly cooked, remove from the pan. Put on a paper towel to cool slightly.

 Add the egg white to the bag with the remaining corn meal. Close the bag. Mush the corn meal mixture with your fingers to mix thoroughly.

 Drop spoonfuls of this dough into the oil and cook for about 4 minutes on each side, until a little brown and puffed. Serve with the cucumber, strawberries and lemon on the side.

SHARE THIS MEAL WITH FRIENDS AND FAMILY

Ingredients			
chicken breast	4 ounces	6 ounces	8 ounces
egg white	2	3	4
corn meal	1/4 cup	3/8 cup	1/2 cup
cucumber	1/2	3/4	1
strawberries	2 cups	3 cups	4 cups
extra-light olive oil	1/2 cup	3/4 cup	1 cup
salt	2 dashes	3 dashes	4 dashes
red pepper	2 dashes	3 dashes	4 dashes
black pepper	2 dashes	3 dashes	4 dashes
lemon wedge	2 wedges	3 wedges	4 wedges

BBQ KEBOBS

You need:
- small bowl
- small sharp knife
- spatula
- broiler pan
- measuring spoons
- skewers

Shopping List
chicken breast
snow peas
onion
zucchini
red pepper
broccoli
cherry tomatoes
mushrooms
extra-light olive oil
salt
dried parsley
lemon

1 2 ounces chicken breast, cut in pieces

2
6 snow peas	4 pieces broccoli
2 wedges of onion	6 cherry tomatoes
3 slices zucchini	2 whole mushrooms
3 pieces red pepper	

3 2/3 teaspoon extra-light olive oil

PLUS!
dash of salt
1 teaspoon dried parsley
2 lemon wedges

EASY! OUCH! HOT!

 Soak the wooden skewers in water.

 Cut the vegetables into wedges.

 In a small bowl, mix the olive oil, salt, and parsley. Add the vegetables and stir to coat.

 Arrange the chicken and vegetables on the skewers. Make your own design. Use all the chicken and vegetables to fill the two skewers.

 Barbecue or broil the kebobs for 2-3 minutes on each side. Use a spatula or fork to turn them—the skewers may get very hot.

 Serve with lemon wedges on the side.

SHARE THIS MEAL WITH FRIENDS AND FAMILY

Ingredients			
chicken breast	4 ounces	6 ounces	8 ounces
snow peas	12	18	24
onion wedges	4	6	8
zucchini slices	6	9	12
red pepper pieces	6	9	12
broccoli pieces	8	12	16
cherry tomatoes	12	18	24
mushrooms	4	6	8
extra-light olive oil	1⅓ teaspoons	2 teaspoons	2⅔ teaspoons
salt	2 dashes	3 dashes	3 dashes
dried parsley	2 teaspoons	1 tablespoon	4 teaspoons
lemon wedges	4 wedges	6 wedges	8 wedges

MIGHTY NICE TOFU STIR FRY

You need:
small sharp knife
spatula
sauté pan
measuring cups
measuring spoons

Shopping List
extra-firm tofu
broccoli
mung beans
snow peas
kiwis
cherries
extra-light olive oil
onion
low salt tamari
lemon

 4 ounces extra-firm tofu

1/2 cup broccoli

 1/2 cup mung beans
1/4 cup snow peas
1 kiwi
5 cherries

 2/3 teaspoon extra-light olive oil

 PLUS! 1 teaspoon chopped onion
1 teaspoon low salt tamari
1 lemon wedge

EASY! OUCH! HOT!

  Cut the tofu and broccoli into bite-sized pieces.

  Warm the oil in a sauté pan. Add the tofu, and cook until it is browned.

  Add the broccoli, cover and cook for 3 minutes. Then add the snow peas and sprouts. Stir for about one minute more.

  Add the garlic, lemon, ginger, and low salt tamari. Stir to coat. Remove from the heat and serve.

  Peel the kiwi and cut into pieces. Put the kiwi and cherries on the plate.

SHARE THIS MEAL WITH FRIENDS AND FAMILY

Ingredients			
extra-firm tofu	8 ounces	12 ounces	1 pound
broccoli	1 cup	1½ cups	2 cups
mung beans	1 cup	1½ cups	2 cups
snow peas	½ cup	¾ cup	1 cup
kiwis	2	3	4
cherries	10	15	20
extra-light olive oil	1⅓ teaspoons	2 teaspoons	2⅔ teaspoons
chopped onion	2 teaspoons	1 tablespoon	4 teaspoons
low salt tamari	2 teaspoons	1 tablespoon	4 teaspoons
lemon wedges	2 wedges	3 wedges	4 wedges

SPAGHETTI AND MEATBALLS

PREP TIME: 10 MINUTES
COOK TIME: 30 MINUTES

family size portion, pictured

You need:
- small bowl
- small sharp knife
- spatula
- frying pan
- measuring cups
- measuring spoons
- oven or microwave

Shopping List

- turkey, chicken, or beef
- spaghetti squash
- tomato sauce
- onion
- peaches
- extra-light olive oil
- Italian seasoning
- parmesan cheese

 2 ounces ground turkey, chicken or lean beef

 1 cup cooked spaghetti squash
1/4 cup tomato sauce
1/8 teaspoon chopped onion
1/2 peach

 2/3 teaspoon extra-light olive oil

 PLUS! Italian seasoning to taste
sprinkle of parmesan cheese

 In a small bowl, combine the meat, onions and roll into balls. Heat the oil in a frying pan and place the meatballs. Cook until browned evenly.

 Cook the spaghetti squash until tender.

 Warm the tomato sauce. When done, pour over the spaghetti squash and meatballs.

 Sprinkle with cheese and seasonings.

 Slice the peach and serve for dessert.

To cook the squash: Microwave the whole squash for 4-5 minutes (this makes it easier to cut in half). Take out and cut in half to remove the seeds. Put the squash cut side down in the microwave with enough water to cover the bottom of the dish. Microwave for 15-20 minutes.

SHARE THIS MEAL WITH FRIENDS AND FAMILY

Ingredients			
turkey, chicken or beef	4 ounces	6 ounces	8 ounces
spaghetti squash	2 cups	3 cups	4 cups
tomato sauce	½ cup	¾ cup	1 cup
chopped onion	¼ teaspoon	⅜ teaspoon	½ teaspoon
peaches	1	1½	2
extra-light olive oil	1⅓ teaspoons	2 teaspoons	2⅔ teaspoons
Italian seasoning	to taste	to taste	to taste
parmesan cheese	2 sprinkles	3 sprinkles	4 sprinkles

MEATLOAF

PREP TIME: 10 MINUTES
COOK TIME: 30 MINUTES

You need:
small bowl
small sharp knife
spatula
baking pan
sauce pan
measuring cups
measuring spoons

Shopping List
ground turkey or beef
turkey or beef stock
carrots
celery
tomato puree
green beans
peaches
extra-light olive oil
cornstarch
garlic cloves
dried basil
dried oregano
dried thyme
dried marjoram
onion powder

1
3 ounces ground turkey, or lean ground beef
1/2 cup turkey or beef stock

2
1/4 cup carrots, diced fine
1 cup celery, diced fine
3/4 cup tomato puree
1 cup green beans
1/2 peach

3
2/3 teaspoon extra-light olive oil

PLUS!
2 teaspoons cornstarch
1 garlic clove, minced
1 teaspoon dried basil
1 teaspoon dried oregano
1 teaspoon dried thyme
1/4 teaspoon dried marjoram
1/8 teaspoon onion powder

 1 Pre-heat oven to 375°. In a small bowl, mix together the turkey or beef, carrots, celery, and ½ tomato puree.

 2 Add 2 garlic cloves, ¼ teaspoon basil, ¼ teaspoon oregano, thyme, and marjoram.

3 Put into an oblong meatloaf baking pan. Bake for 30-35 minutes.

 4 In a saucepan, steam the green beans until slightly tender, do not overcook.

 5 In a saucepan, combine oil, stock, tomato puree, basil, oregano, garlic, onion powder, and cornstarch to make an Italian sauce. Lightly simmer until it thickens.

 6 Remove the meatloaf from the pan. Pour the Italian sauce over the meatloaf. Serve the peach for dessert.

SHARE THIS MEAL WITH FRIENDS AND FAMILY

Ingredients			
ground turkey or beef	6 ounces	9 ounces	12 ounces
turkey or beef stock	1 cup	1½ cups	2 cups
carrots	½ cup	¾ cup	1 cup
celery	2 cups	3 cups	4 cups
tomato puree	1½ cups	2¼ cups	3 cups
green beans	2 cups	3 cups	4 cups
peaches	1	1½	2
extra-light olive oil	1⅓ teaspoons	2 teaspoons	2⅔ teaspoons
cornstarch	4 teaspoons	2 tablespoons	8 teaspoons
garlic cloves	2	3	4
dried basil	2 teaspoons	1 tablespoon	4 teaspoons
dried oregano	2 teaspoons	1 tablespoon	4 teaspoons
dried thyme	2 teaspoons	1 tablespoon	4 teaspoons
dried marjoram	½ teaspoon	¾ teaspoon	1 teaspoon
onion powder	¼ teaspoon	⅜ teaspoon	½ teaspoon

WHAT ARE YOU EATING?

With our hectic schedules we often order fast food, convincing ourselves that it must be healthy because it is chicken, pasta or stir-fry. Television advertisements, peer pressure, and the smell of trans fats seduce us. The rate of obesity is growing at an alarming rate. Everyone is talking about exercise, surgery, and genetics, but few look at the amount of carbohydrates in our diets. When diet is discussed and change is recommended, many balk at giving up foods they are used to eating. Therefore, many refuse to acknowledge their need for healthy foods.

Lots of trans fat in this meal—your body has to fight hard to stay healthy!

I can't hang on with this fat!

I am having trouble hanging on!

HELP! Please add some protein!

Chicken Nuggets		6 pieces		*4 sugar cubes
Protein 15 Grams	😊😊😊😊😊😊😊😊😊😊😊😊😊😊😊😊			
Carbohydrates 16 Grams				
Sugar 7 Cubes	⬜⬜⬜⬜⬜⬜⬜			
Glycemic Index 66				
Glycemic Load 66x 16/100=11	✺✺✺✺✺			
Effective Sugar Cube Load-5				
Total Fat 20 Grams	(fat droplet symbols ×16 and additional row ×3)			
Saturated Fat 4 Grams	(4 symbols)			
Trans Fat	🚫			
Sodium (each=50mg) 513 mg	(11 sodium piles)			

Snacks

A well-balanced snack provides an important boost to help you power through your afternoon, and wind down for a restful sleep. Try some of these healthy and tasty choices.

Snacks are an important event of the day!

☆ Make special places in the refrigerator and in the cupboard for snacks.

☆ **Creative minds** need to be refueled after a busy week in school for a busy and fun weekend.

☆ Put ingredients together in a special pre-assigned place so everyone can create **balanced** snacks.

☆ Snacks can be **leftovers** from special meals.

☆ Make sure there are lots of **snacks** available, especially if dinner is going to be late. You don't want to go more than five hours without eating.

☆ Always have a bedtime snack. It is at least eight hours until your next meal!

HIGH POWER NUT BUTTER

PREP TIME: 5 MINUTES

 2 cups low fat ricotta cheese

 Check with Omega-2 and add a carbohydrate when you eat this!

 1 tablespoon plus 1 teaspoon nut butter (peanut, almond, cashew or macadamia)

 Blend the ricotta cheese and nut butter in the food processor or by hand. (This doesn't work well in a blender.)

 You can make this ahead and store it in the refrigerator until you eat it.

 Put on muffins, fruit, such as apples or pears, celery sticks, or get creative and discover new uses.

You need:
large bowl
spatula
measuring spoons
storage container

Shopping List
low-fat ricotta cheese
nut butter

 *This recipe makes enough High Power Nut Butter to have on hand for many different snacks!*

SHARE THIS MEAL WITH FRIENDS AND FAMILY

Ingredients	👫	👫	👫👫
low-fat ricotta cheese	4 cups	6 cups	8 cups
nut butter	8 teaspoons	1/4 cup	16 teaspoons

MIGHTY YUMMY COCOA

EASY! HOT!

You need:
blender
measuring cups
measuring spoons

 1 cup milk

 ⅛ cup whey protein powder

 2 tablespoons unsweetened cocoa powder
1 tablespoon fructose
5 drops liquid stevia✿

 ⅔ teaspoon extra-light olive oil

 ½ teaspoon vanilla extract
pinch salt

 Put the milk in a sauce pan and and warm.

 In a blender, combine the chocolate, fructose, liquid stevia, vanilla and salt.

 Add ½ cup of milk. Blend until smooth. Add the rest of the milk. Serve immediately.

✿ To find the liquid stevia supplement, see page 200.

Shopping List
milk
whey protein powder
unsweetened cocoa powder
fructose
stevia
extra-light olive oil
vanilla extract
salt

SHARE THIS MEAL WITH FRIENDS AND FAMILY

Ingredients	👥	👥	👥👥
milk	2 cups	3 cups	4 cups
whey protein powder	¼ cup	⅜ cup	½ cup
unsweetened cocoa powder	¼ cup	6 tablespoons	½ cup
fructose	⅛ cup	3 tablespoons	¼ cup
stevia	10 drops	15 drops	20 drops
extra-light olive oil	1⅓ teaspoons	2 teaspoons	2⅔ teaspoons
vanilla extract	1 teaspoon	1½ teaspoons	2 teaspoons
salt	2 pinches	3 pinches	4 pinches

MELON & PROTEIN

PREP TIME: 8 MINUTES
COOK TIME: 3 MINUTES

 ½ cup low fat plain yogurt

 1 ounce Canadian bacon, 3 strips turkey bacon, 2 soy sausage links or ⅛ cup whey protein powder

 ¼ cantaloupe, or ¼ honeydew melon

 1 ⅓ tablespoon slivered almonds

 Place the yogurt and stevia in a bowl and mix well. If using protein powder, mix in with yogurt.

 If using Canadian bacon, turkey bacon or soy links, do not use the protein powder. Cook in a frying pan.

Cut the melon in half. Remove the seeds. Place the yogurt in the center of the melon.

You need:
small bowl
small sharp knife
measuring cups
measuring spoons

Shopping List

low fat plain yogurt
Canadian bacon or
turkey bacon or
soy sausage links or
whey protein powder
cantaloupe or honeydew
slivered almonds

SHARE THIS MEAL WITH FRIENDS AND FAMILY

Ingredients			
low fat plain yogurt	1 cup	1½ cups	2 cups
Canadian bacon OR	2 ounces	3 ounces	4 ounces
turkey bacon OR	6 strips	9 strips	12 strips
soy sausage links OR	4 links	6 links	8 links
whey protein powder	¼ cup	⅜ cup	½ cup
cantaloupe	½	¾	1
honeydew melon	½	¾	1
slivered almonds	2⅔ tablespoons	4 tablespoons	5⅓ tablespoons

SPICY CORN MUFFIN MELT

EASY! OUCH! HOT!

PREP TIME: 5 MINUTES
COOK TIME: 3 MINUTES

 2 corn muffins. See recipe, page 180

 1 ounce shredded mozzarella cheese

 2 tablespoons tomato salsa

 2/3 teaspoon extra-light olive oil

PLUS! pinch red pepper flakes

 Slice each muffin crosswise to make 4 half muffins.

 Put a little olive oil on each muffin and sprinkle with a tiny bit of red pepper flakes. Put the cut side face up on a toaster oven pan.

 Top each with shredded cheese and melt in a toaster oven or broiler for 3-4 minutes.

 Serve with the salsa on the side. Dip the muffin into the salsa.

You need:
small knife
broiler or toaster oven
measuring cups
measuring spoons

Shopping List

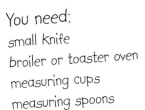

shredded mozzarella cheese
tomato salsa
extra-light olive oil
red pepper flakes

SHARE THIS MEAL WITH FRIENDS AND FAMILY

Ingredients			
corn muffins	4	6	8
mozzarella cheese	2 ounces	3 ounces	4 ounces
tomato salsa	1/4 cup	6 tablespoons	1/2 cup
extra-light olive oil	1 1/3 teaspoons	2 teaspoons	2 2/3 teaspoons
red pepper flakes	2 pinches	3 pinches	4 pinches

Powerful Food for Powerful Minds & Bodies 159

TURKEY & CHEESE TREAT

PREP TIME: 3 MINUTES
COOK TIME: 2 MINUTES

You need:
broiler or toaster oven
measuring spoons

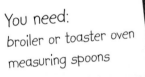

Shopping List
low fat cheese
sliced turkey
recommended bread
pizza sauce
extra-light olive oil
oregano

 1 ounce low fat cheese
1 piece sliced turkey

 1 slice recommended bread
1 tablespoon pizza sauce

 2/3 teaspoon extra-light olive oil

PLUS! sprinkle of oregano

 Spread the olive oil evenly on the outside of the bread.

 Spread the pizza sauce on top of the bread. Put the cheese and meat on top of the sauce.

 Sprinkle the oregano on top of the cheese.

 Put under the broiler or toaster oven until the cheese is melted.

 French Meadow Bakery:
Men's Bread
Women's Bread

SHARE THIS MEAL WITH FRIENDS AND FAMILY

Ingredients	👫	👫	👫👫
low fat cheese	2 ounces	3 ounces	4 ounces
sliced turkey	2 slices	3 slices	4 slices
recommended bread	2 slices	3 slices	4 slices
pizza sauce	2 tablespoons	3 tablespoons	4 tablespoons
extra-light olice oil	1⅓ teaspoons	2 teaspoons	2⅔ teaspoons
oregano	2 sprinkles	3 sprinkles	4 sprinkles

CRUNCHY ALMOND SNACK

EASY!

 1 power pancake, 4" across, see power pancake recipe page 58

 1/2 fresh pear

 1 teaspoon high power nut butter, see recipe page 156
1/2 teaspoon slivered almonds

 pinch of cinnamon

You need:
measuring cups
measuring spoons
small knife

 Spread the high power nut butter on the pancake.

 Sprinkle with almonds and cinnamon.

 Roll the pancake and slice in quarters.

 Slice the pear. Sprinkle with cinnamon.

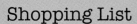

Shopping List
pears
slivered almonds
cinnamon

SHARE THIS MEAL WITH FRIENDS AND FAMILY

Ingredients	👥	👥	👥👤
pancakes	2	3	4
pears	1	1½	2
high power nut butter	2 teaspoons	1 tablespoon	4 teaspoons
slivered almonds	1 teaspoon	1½ teaspoons	2 teaspoons
cinnamon	2 pinches	3 pinches	4 pinches

NUTTY BANANA SNACK

EASY!

 1 power pancake, 4" across, see power pancake recipe, page 58

 ⅓ fresh banana, sliced in long sticks

 1 teaspoon high power nut butter, see recipe, page 156

 Spread the high power nut butter on the pancake.

 Put the banana pieces on top, all going in the same direction.

Roll the pancake and enjoy.

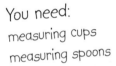
You need:
measuring cups
measuring spoons

Shopping List
bananas

SHARE THIS MEAL WITH FRIENDS AND FAMILY

Ingredients	👥	👥	👥👤
pancakes	2	3	4
bananas	⅔	1	1⅓
high power nut butter	2 teaspoons	1 tablespoon	4 teaspoons

MIGHTY NICE DEVILED EGGS

COOK TIME: 10 MINUTES
PREP TIME: 2 MINUTES

EASY! OUCH! HOT!

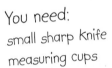

You need:
small sharp knife
measuring cups

Shopping List
eggs
hummus
paprika

 2 hard-boiled egg whites

 ⅓ cup hummus

PLUS! sprinkle of paprika

1 Hard boil the eggs. When done, put in cool water to stop cooking. Peel the eggs, cut lengthwise and remove the yolks.

2 Stuff each egg white with the hummus mixture.

3 Sprinkle with paprika to taste.

 Be creative with the many flavors of hummus. Choose your favorite or experiment with other kinds and you will think you have a totally different snack. Cook eggs ahead of time so you can make a fast and easy snack anytime.

SHARE THIS MEAL WITH FRIENDS AND FAMILY

Ingredients			
hard boiled egg whites	4	6	8
hummus	⅔ cup	1 cup	1⅓ cups
paprika	2 sprinkles	3 sprinkles	4 sprinkles

Powerful Food for Powerful Minds & Bodies

CHEESE & FRUIT

PREP TIME: 2 MINUTES

 1 piece low fat string cheese

 ½ apple, ½ pear or 1 peach

 ½ teaspoon nut butter

You need:
small sharp knife
measuring spoons

Shopping List
low fat string cheese
apples, pears, or peaches
nut butter

Cut the fruit in half. Take out the seeds.

Spread the nut butter on the fruit.

Serve with the string cheese.

Try different types of nut butter. Besides peanut, there is almond, cashew, macadamia, pecan, and walnut, or try combinations of them.

SHARE THIS MEAL WITH FRIENDS AND FAMILY

Ingredients	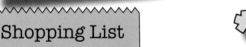		
string cheese	2 pieces	3 pieces	4 pieces
apples	1	1½	2
pears	1	1½	2
peaches	2	3	4
nut butter	1 teaspoon	1½ teaspoons	2 teaspoons

COTTAGE CHEESE AND FRUIT

EASY!

PREP TIME: 3 MINUTES

 ¹/₄ cup cottage cheese

 ¹/₂ cup pineapple ✿

 1 ¹/₃ teaspoon slivered almonds

PLUS! 5 drops stevia ✿

 Put the cottage cheese in a small bowl.

 Add the pineapple, and stevia and mix thoroughly.

 Sprinkle with slivered almonds.

✿ Use different kinds of fruit for variety.

Check with Me!

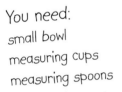

You need:
small bowl
measuring cups
measuring spoons

Shopping List

cottage cheese
pineapple
slivered almonds
stevia

✿ To find the stevia supplement, see page 200.

SHARE THIS MEAL WITH FRIENDS AND FAMILY.

Ingredients	👥	👥	👥👤
cottage cheese	¹/₂ cup	³/₄ cup	1 cup
pineapple	1 cup	1¹/₂ cups	2 cups
slivered almonds	2²/₃ teaspoons	4 teaspoons	5¹/₃ teaspoons
stevia	10 drops	15 drops	20 drops

TURKEY LOG AND APPLE

PREP TIME: 2 MINUTES

You need:
small knife
measuring spoons

 1 1/2 ounces sliced turkey

 1/2 apple

 1/2 teaspoon nut butter

 Roll the turkey into a log.

 Slice an apple in half and take out the seeds.

 Spread the nut butter on the apple.

Shopping List
sliced turkey
apples
nut butter

SHARE THIS MEAL WITH FRIENDS AND FAMILY

Ingredients	👫	👫	👫👤
sliced turkey	3 ounces	4 1/2 ounces	6 ounces
apples	1	1 1/2	2
nut butter	1 teaspoon	1 1/2 teaspoons	2 teaspoons

MELTED CHEESE AND CRACKER

PREP TIME: 2 MINUTES

You need:
small sharp knife
broiler or toaster oven

Shopping List
low fat shredded cheese
Wasa crackers
olives

 1 ounce low fat shredded cheese

 1 Wasa cracker

 5 olives, sliced

 Slice the olives. Place on top of the cracker.

 Place the cheese on top of the olives.

 Put in broiler to melt the cheese.

SHARE THIS MEAL WITH FRIENDS AND FAMILY

Ingredients	👥	👥	👥👤
low fat shredded cheese	2 ounces	3 ounces	4 ounces
Wasa crackers	2	3	4
sliced olives	10	15	20

MIGHTY NICE NACHOS

PREP TIME: 5 MINUTES
COOK TIME: 2 MINUTES

 EASY! HOT!

 1 tablespoon shredded cheddar cheese
1 ounce ground turkey, or beef

 6 nacho chips
2 tablespoons salsa

 1 tablespoon avocado or guacamole

 Place the chips on a cookie sheet.

 On each chip, place cheese, turkey, or beef and top with the avocado.

 Put salsa on each chip.

 Place under the broiler to melt the cheese.

You need:
cookie sheet
broiler oven
measuring cups
measuring spoons

Shopping List
shredded cheddar cheese
ground turkey or beef
nacho chips
salsa
avocado or guacamole

SHARE THIS MEAL WITH FRIENDS AND FAMILY

Ingredients	👥	👥	👥👥
shredded cheddar cheese	2 tablespoons	3 tablespoons	1/4 cup
ground turkey/beef	2 ounces	3 ounces	4 ounces
nacho chips	12	18	24
salsa	1/4 cup	6 tablespoons	1/2 cup
avocado or guacamole	2 tablespoons	3 tablespoons	1/4 cup

TOASTED CHEESE PANWICH

PREP TIME: 5 MINUTES
COOK TIME: 5 MINUTES

You need:
medium skillet
measuring spoons

Shopping List
sliced cheddar cheese
sliced mozzarella cheese
strawberries
blueberries
extra-light olive oil

 2 power pancakes, about 4" in size, see recipe, page 58

 1 slice cheddar cheese
1 slice mozzarella cheese

 ½ cup strawberries
¼ cup blueberries

 ⅓ teaspoon extra-light olive oil

 Spread the olive oil evenly on the outside of each pancake.

 Place the pancake, oil side down, on a medium skillet. Put the cheese on top of the pancake.

 Put the second pancake on top, oil side up.

 Cook until the cheese starts to melt. Then turn over and cook until the cheese is melted.

 Serve the fruit on the side.

SHARE THIS MEAL WITH FRIENDS AND FAMILY.

Ingredients	👥	👥	👥👤
power pancakes	4	6	8
sliced cheddar cheese	2 slices	3 slices	4 slices
sliced mozzarella cheese	2 slices	3 slices	4 slices
strawberries	1 cup	1½ cups	2 cups
blueberries	½ cup	¾ cup	1 cup
extra-light olive oil	⅔ teaspoon	1 teaspoon	1⅓ teaspoons

SNACKS—WHAT ARE YOU EATING?

Snacks are very important during the day in order to keep insulin stable, and maintain balanced energy levels. What is so detrimental is the type of snack foods most people eat. The high sugar snacks activate insulin. High insulin lowers the blood sugar, which leads to sugar cravings, and the cycle begins. The high and low sugar values cause lack of concentration, poor memory, and lowered immune systems.

With the amount of sugar and salt you would have to eat a lot of protein!

Pretzels	8 ounces	*89 Sugar Cubes
Carbohydrates 172 Grams		
Sugar 75 Cubes		
Glycemic Index 119		
Glycemic Load 119 x172/100=205		
Effective Sugar Cube Load-89		
Total Fat 8 Grams		
Monounsaturated Fat-3 Grams		
Saturated Fat-2 Grams		
Trans Fat		
Sodium (each=50mg) 3890 mg		

Potato Chips											8 ounces			*50 sugar cubes	
Carbohydrates 110 Grams															
Sugar 48 Cubes															
Glycemic Index 104															
Glycemic Load 104 x 110/100=114															
Effective Sugar Cube Load-50															
Total Fat 79 Grams															
Monounsaturated Fat-22 Grams															
Saturated Fat-25 Grams															
Trans Fat															
Sodium (each=50mg) 1348 mg															

Watch out, especially if you add a large cola drink—you're asking for trouble!

Corn Chips — 8 ounces — *57 sugar cubes

Carbohydrates 118 Grams	
Sugar 51 Cubes	
Glycemic Index 110	
Glycemic Load 110 x118/100=130	
Effective Sugar Cube Load-57	
Total Fat 76 Grams	
Monounsaturated Fat-22 Grams	
Saturated Fat-10 Grams	
Trans Fat	
Sodium (each=50mg) 1429 mg	

Chocolate Bar, Milk — 2.3 ounces — *10 sugar cubes

Protein 5 Grams	
Carbohydrates 37 Grams	
Sugar 16 Cubes	
Glycemic Index 64	
Glycemic Load 64 x 37/100=24	
Effective Sugar Cube Load-10	
Total Fat 20 Grams	
Monounsaturated Fat-9 Grams	
Saturated Fat-9 Grams	
Sodium (each=50mg) 52 mg	
Caffeine 13 mg	

WOULD YOU EVER GUESS....

When you see the composition of these fast foods, that seem so tasty, you will be surprised. When you think about eating them, just visualize the bowl of sugar and fat that you are really eating. Feel the squishy texture of the fat and the gritty taste of the sugar! How healthy is this?

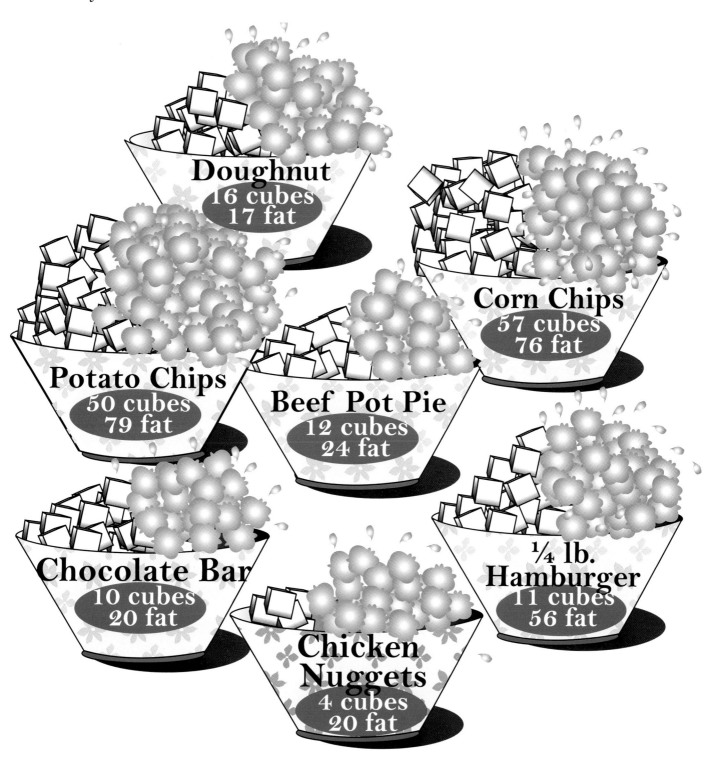

Doughnut
16 cubes
17 fat

Corn Chips
57 cubes
76 fat

Potato Chips
50 cubes
79 fat

Beef Pot Pie
12 cubes
24 fat

Chocolate Bar
10 cubes
20 fat

Chicken Nuggets
4 cubes
20 fat

¼ lb. Hamburger
11 cubes
56 fat

WEEKEND TREATS

Cooking and baking are wonderful weekend activities to bring your family together. Parents and children can make these delicious recipes in advance to enjoy throughout the week, or eat them right out of the oven.

Weekends can be fun creative times!

⭐ Get the entire family involved in meal planning. Each member can be in charge of one week of the month.

⭐ Make sure when you use an ingredient you add it to the shopping list during the week. This saves time over the weekend.

⭐ Make shopping a family affair and an educational one also. Make sure everyone reads the ingredients.

⭐ Have everyone in the family be in charge of one part of the meal. For example, one can be in charge of protein, one in charge of carbohydrate, and one in charge of fat.

⭐ Give a special prize for the best creative idea.

⭐ **Remember the chef of the family is the pharmacist of the family. The food you eat can bring about good health or can provide the environment for to create disease.**

MIGHTY NUTTY PIE CRUSTS

PREP TIME: 15 MINUTES
COOK TIME: 15 MINUTES

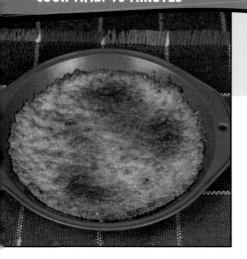

You need:
medium bowl
blender
spatula
measuring spoons
measuring cups
9 inch pie plate

ALMOND CRUST

 EASY! HOT!

1. 1 egg white

2. ¼ cup fructose

3. 1½ cups blanched almonds

1. Preheat the oven to 375° F.

2. Chop the almonds in a food processsor or use a knife to chop into small pieces.

3. Beat the egg white until stiff. Gradually fold in the fructose. Add the chopped almonds. Press the mixture firmly over the bottom and sides of an oiled 9-inch pie plate. Bake the shell until it becomes light brown. Remove to a rack and cool.

BRAZIL NUT CRUST

1. 1 egg white

2. 2 tablespoons fructose

3. 1 cup chopped Brazil nuts

1. Preheat the oven to 400° F. Chop enough Brazil nuts to make 1 cup.

2. Blend the ground nuts, and egg white with the fructose. Press the mixture against the bottom and sides of a 9-inch pie plate.

3. Bake the shell until it becomes light brown, about 8 minutes. Cool.

APPLESAUCE MUFFINS

PREP TIME: 15 MINUTES
COOK TIME: 15 MINUTES

You need:
2 bowls
measuring cups
measuring spoons
wire whisk
muffin tin

Shopping List
low fat buttermilk
whey protein powder
egg whites
oat flour
barley flour
unsweetened applesauce
fructose
extra-light olive oil
chopped nuts
baking powder
baking soda
cinnamon
salt
vanilla extract

 2/3 cup low fat buttermilk

 3/4 cup whey protein powder
1/4 cup egg whites

 1/2 cup oat flour
1/4 cup barley flour
2/3 cup unsweetened applesauce
2 tablespoons fructose

 1/4 cup extra-light olive oil
1/2 cup chopped nuts

Extra dry ingredients:
 1 teaspoon baking powder
1 teaspoon baking soda
1 tablespoon cinnamon
1/4 teaspoon salt
Extra wet ingredients
1 1/2 tablespoons vanilla extract

 1 Preheat the oven to 350° F. Wipe oil into the cups of a 12 cup muffin tin.

 2 Mix the dry ingredients together (whey protein powder, oat flour, barley flour, fructose, nuts, baking powder, baking soda, cinnamon and salt).

 3 Whisk together wet ingredients (buttermilk, egg whites, applesauce, olive oil and vanilla).

 4 Gently add the dry ingredients. Stir until blended. Do not over-mix as you will get tough muffins.

 5 Pour the batter into the muffin tins. Bake for 15–18 minutes.

SHARE THIS MEAL WITH FRIENDS AND FAMILY

Ingredients			
low fat buttermilk	1⅓ cups	2 cups	2⅔ cups
whey protein powder	1½ cups	3 cups	4½ cups
egg whites	½ cup	¾ cup	1 cup
oat flour	1 cup	1½ cups	2 cups
barley flour	½ cup	¾ cup	1 cup
unsweetened applesauce	1⅓ cups	2 cups	2⅔ cups
fructose	¼ cup	6 tablespoons	½ cup
extra-light olive oil	½ cup	¾ cup	1 cup
chopped nuts	1 cup	1½ cups	2 cups
baking powder	2 teaspoons	1 tablespoon	4 teaspoons
baking soda	2 teaspoons	1 tablespoon	4 teaspoons
cinnamon	2 tablespoons	3 tablespoons	¼ cup
salt	½ teaspoon	¾ teaspoon	1 teaspoon
vanilla extract	3 tablespoons	4½ tablespoons	6 tablespoons

CRISPY POTATO SKINS

PREP TIME: 5 MINUTES
COOK TIME: 60 MINUTES

EASY! OUCH! HOT!

 Caution: Make sure you add a protein!

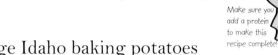 Make sure you add a protein to make this recipe complete!

 3 large Idaho baking potatoes

3 1 cup extra-light olive oil

1 Preheat the oven to 425°F. Thoroughly wash and dry the potatoes.

2 Place on a rack in the oven and bake until tender when tested with a fork, 40-60 minutes.

3 When the potatoes are done, remove from the oven. Cut them in half and let cool.

4 Scoop out the inside of the potato and save for the Mighty Potato Cakes, see recipe, page 110.

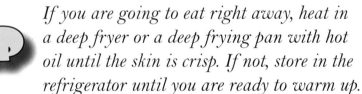 *If you are going to eat right away, heat in a deep fryer or a deep frying pan with hot oil until the skin is crisp. If not, store in the refrigerator until you are ready to warm up.*

You need:
storage container
small sharp knife
measuring cups

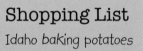
Shopping List
Idaho baking potatoes
extra-light olive oil

SHARE THIS MEAL WITH FRIENDS AND FAMILY

Ingredients	👥	👥	👥👥
Idaho baking potatoes	6	9	12
extra-light olive oil	2 cups	3 cups	4 cups

ALMOND COOKIES

 1 1/2 cup egg whites

 2 4 teaspoons fructose

 3 2/3 cup ground almonds

EASY! HOT!

You need:
coffee grinder
spatula
electric mixer
measuring cups
measuring spoons

Shopping List
egg whites
fructose
almonds

 1 Preheat oven to 275°F.

 2 Beat the egg whites with an electric mixer, starting on low for one minute. Then turn to high for about four more minutes.

 3 Sprinkle the fructose over the egg whites one teaspoon at a time. Beat with the mixer for about 30 seconds in between each teaspoon of fructose. (Whipped egg and fructose is called a meringue.)

 4 Grind the nuts in the coffee grinder. With a rubber spatula, gently fold in the ground nuts by sprinkling them over the meringue.

 5 Drop spoonfuls on a foil covered baking sheet, one inch apart. Put about 12 cookies on a baking sheet. This recipe makes enough for two baking sheets.

 6 Bake for one hour at 275°F.

SHARE THIS MEAL WITH FRIENDS AND FAMILY

Ingredients	👥	👥👤	👥👥
egg whites	1 cup	1½ cups	2 cups
fructose	8 teaspoons	4 tablespoons	16 teaspoons
ground almonds	1⅓ cups	2 cups	2⅔ cups

CORN MUFFINS

You need:
2 small bowls
wire whisk
spatula
measuring cups
measuring spoons

Shopping List
low fat buttermilk
whey protein powder
egg whites
oat flour
corn meal
fresh or frozen corn
unsweetened applesauce
extra-light olive oil
baking powder
salt
stevia
vanilla extract

 1 cup low fat buttermilk

 3/4 cup whey protein powder
1/2 cup egg whites

 1/3 cup oat flour
3/4 cup corn meal
1/2 cup fresh or frozen corn kernels
1/3 cup unsweetened applesauce

 1/4 cup extra-light olive oil

 2 teaspoons baking powder
1/4 teaspoon salt
10 drops stevia✿
1 teaspoon vanilla extract

✿ To find the stevia supplement, see page 200.

 1 Preheat the oven to 350°F. Wipe oil into the cups of a 12 cup muffin tin.

 2 Mix the dry ingredients (whey protein powder, oat flour, corn meal, corn kernels, baking powder, and salt) and set aside.

 3 Whisk together wet ingredients (buttermilk, egg whites, applesauce, extra-light olive oil, stevia and vanilla). Gently add the dry ingredients. Stir until blended.

 4 Pour into 12 muffin cups and bake for 15-18 minutes.

SHARE THIS MEAL WITH FRIENDS AND FAMILY

Ingredients			
low fat buttermilk	2 cups	3 cups	4 cups
whey protein powder	1½ cups	2¼ cups	3 cups
egg whites	1 cup	1½ cups	2 cups
oat flour	⅔ cup	1 cup	1⅓ cups
corn meal	1½ cups	2¼ cups	3 cups
fresh or frozen corn	1 cup	1½ cups	2 cups
unsweetened applesauce	⅔ cup	1 cup	1⅓ cups
extra-light olive oil	½ cup	¾ cup	1 cup
baking powder	4 teaspoons	2 tablespoons	8 teaspoons
salt	½ teaspoon	¾ teaspoon	1 teaspoon
stevia	15 drops	20 drops	25 drops
vanilla extract	2 teaspoons	1 tablespoon	4 teaspoons

CHOCOLATE PUDDING

PREP TIME: 15 MINUTES
COOK TIME: 15 MINUTES

You need:
pudding bowls
spatula
sauce pan
measuring cups
measuring spoons

Shopping List

low fat milk
whey protein powder
arrowroot powder
fructose
unsweetened cocoa
extra-light olive oil
vanilla extract

 ½ cup low fat milk

 1 tablespoon whey protein powder

2 teaspoons arrowroot powder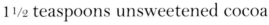
1 tablespoon fructose
1½ teaspoons unsweetened cocoa

 ⅔ teaspoon extra-light olive oil

PLUS! 1 teaspoon vanilla extract

 If you have trouble finding arrowroot powder, you can use cornstarch.

 In the saucepan, whisk together the milk, whey protein powder, arrowroot powder, fructose and cocoa.

 Cook over medium heat, stirring frequently with the whisk. When the pudding starts to boil, whisk for one more minute.

 Remove from the heat. Put the vanilla extract in a small bowl. Add the extra-light oil and stir together. Stir into the pudding.

 Pour into a bowl to cool. Chill until you are ready to eat.

SHARE THIS MEAL WITH FRIENDS AND FAMILY

Ingredients	👥	👥	👥👤
low fat milk	1 cup	1½ cups	2 cups
whey protein powder	⅛ cup	3 tablespoons	¼ cup
arrowroot powder	4 teaspoons	2 tablespoons	8 teaspoons
fructose	⅛ cup	3 tablespoons	¼ cup
unsweetened cocoa	3 teaspoons	4½ teaspoons.	2 tablespoons
extra-light olive oil	1⅓ teaspoons	2 teaspoons	2⅔ teaspoons
vanilla extract	2 teaspoons	1 tablespoon	4 teaspoons

FRUIT FROGURT

You need:
electric mixer and bowl
mixing spoon
sauce pan
measuring cups
measuring spoons

Shopping List
low fat plain yogurt
Knox unflavored gelatin
egg whites
peaches or
strawberries or
raspberries
fructose
slivered almonds
vanilla extract
ginger
allspice
stevia

 1 cup low fat plain yogurt

 1 envelope Knox unflavored gelatin
2 egg whites

 1 peach
3/4 cup strawberries or
3/4 cup raspberries
1 teaspoon fructose

 5 1/3 teaspoons slivered almonds

 1 teaspoon vanilla extract
pinch of ginger
pinch of allspice
5 drops stevia

⊙ To find the stevia supplement, see page 200.

 1 Place yogurt, gelatin, stevia, fruit, spices and vanilla extract into a saucepan. Heat until the mixture becomes warm, not boiling.

 2 Set the mixture aside and let cool.

 3 Put the egg whites into a mixing bowl and whip until firm.

 4 When the liquid has cooled, fold in the whipped egg whites and slivered almonds.

 5 Place mixture in dessert serving dishes and place in the refrigerator.

SHARE THIS MEAL WITH FRIENDS AND FAMILY

Ingredients			
low fat plain yogurt	2 cups	3 cups	4 cups
Knox unflavored gelatin	2 envelopes	3 envelopes	4 envelopes
egg whites	4	6	8
peaches	2	3	4
strawberries	1½ cups	2¼ cups	3 cups
raspberries	1½ cups	2¼ cups	3 cups
fructose	2 teaspoons	1 tablespoon	4 teaspoons
slivered almonds	10⅔ teaspoons	16 teaspoons	21⅓ teaspoons
vanilla extract	2 teaspoons	1 tablespoon	4 teaspoons
ginger	2 pinches	3 pinches	4 pinches
allspice	2 pinches	3 pinches	4 pinches
stevia	10 drops	15 drops	20 drops

MIGHTY OATMEAL MACAROONS

PREP TIME: 15 MINUTES
COOK TIME: 12 MINUTES

You need:
large bowl
metal spatula
measuring cups
measuring spoons
electric mixer and bowl

Shopping List
egg whites
whey protein powder
slow cooking oatmeal
pure maple syrup
fructose
almonds
unsalted butter
dried unsweetened coconut
vanilla extract
sea salt

 4 egg whites, room temperature
1 cup whey protein powder

 1/4 cup slow cooking oatmeal
6 tablespoons pure maple syrup
2 tablespoons fructose

 1/2 cup almond flour
2 tablespoons unsalted butter
3/4 cup dried unsweetened coconut

PLUS! 2 teaspoons vanilla extract
1/2 teaspoon sea salt

EASY! HOT!

 1 Preheat the oven to 350°F.

 2 Put almonds in a coffee grinder or heavy blender to make ½ cup almond flour.

 3 In a large bowl, add the protein powder, oatmeal, dried coconut, almond flour, fructose, and salt.

 4 Add the maple syrup, vanilla extract, and butter. Mix well.

 5 Put the egg whites in a mixing bowl and beat until they are stiff. Fold in with the rest of the ingredients and mix well.

 6 Rub the cookie sheet with butter. Sprinkle with coconut. Place one tablespoon dough per cookie on the sheet. Bake for 12 minutes.

 7 When baked, quickly remove the cookies with a thin metal spatula. As the cookies cool they will be harder to remove from the sheet. Makes about 24 cookies.

SHARE THIS MEAL WITH FRIENDS AND FAMILY

Ingredients			
egg whites	8	12	16
whey protein powder	2 cups	3 cups	4 cups
slow cooking oatmeal	½ cup	¾ cup	1 cup
pure maple syrup	¾ cup	18 tablespoons	1½ cups
fructose	¼ cup	6 tablespoons	½ cup
almond flour	1 cup	1½ cups	2 cups
unsalted butter	¼ cup	6 tablespoons	½ cup
unsweetened coconut	1½ cups	2¼ cups	3 cups
vanilla extract	4 teaspoons	2 tablespoons	8 teaspoons
sea salt	1 teaspoon	1½ teaspoons	2 teaspoons

CHOCOLATE COOKIES

PREP TIME: 15 MINUTES
COOK TIME: 1 HOUR

 1 ½ cup egg whites

 2 4 teaspoons fructose
1 tablespoon unsweetened cocoa

 EASY! HOT!

 3 ⅔ cup finely ground almonds

You need:
electric mixer and bowl
spatula
1 cookie sheet
measuring cups
measuring spoons

Shopping List
egg whites
fructose
unsweetened cocoa
almonds

 1 Preheat oven to 275°F.

 2 Beat the egg whites with an electric mixer, starting on low for one minute. Then turn to high for about four more minutes.

 3 Sprinkle the fructose over the egg whites one teaspoon at a time. Beat with the mixer for about 30 seconds in between each teaspoon of fructose to make a meringue.

 4 Stir together the cocoa, and almonds. With a rubber spatula, gently fold in the mixture by sprinkling it over the meringue.

 5 Using a teaspoon, drop spoonfuls on a foil covered baking sheet, one inch apart. Put about 12 cookies on a baking sheet. This recipe makes enough for 2 baking sheets.

 6 Bake for one hour. You will make 24 two inch cookies.

 For variations of flavors, use different nuts: cashews, macadamia, pecans, walnuts. To grind the nuts, use a coffee grinder or a strong blender.

SHARE THIS MEAL WITH FRIENDS AND FAMILY

Ingredients	👥	👥	👥👤
egg whites	1 cup	1½ cups	2 cups
fructose	8 teaspoons	¼ cup	16 teaspoons
unsweetened cocoa	⅛ cup	3 tablespoons	¼ cup
ground almonds	1⅓ cups	2 cups	2⅔ cups

CINNASAUCE YOGURT

PREP TIME: 8 MINUTES

You need:
medium bowl
spatula
measuring cups
measuring spoons

Shopping List
low-fat plain yogurt
Knox unflavored gelatin
unsweetened applesauce
slivered almonds
ground cinnamon
lemon extract
stevia

 1 cup low fat plain yogurt

 2 envelopes Knox unflavored gelatin

 2/3 cup unsweetened applesauce

 4 teaspoons slivered almonds

 PLUS!
1/2 teaspoon ground cinnamon
1/4 teaspoon lemon extract
5 drops stevia ✿

 In a bowl, mix the yogurt, gelatin, almonds, cinnamon, lemon extract, and stevia.

 Add the applesauce and mix well.

 Put in four dessert serving dishes.

✿ To find the stevia supplement, see page 200.

SHARE THIS MEAL WITH FRIENDS AND FAMILY

Ingredients	👫	👫	👫👤
low-fat plain yogurt	2 cups	3 cups	4 cups
Knox unflavored gelatin	4 envelopes	6 envelopes	8 envelopes
unsweetened applesauce	1⅓ cups	2 cups	2⅔ cups
slivered almonds	8 teaspoons	4 tablespoons	16 teaspoons
ground cinnamon	1 teaspoon	1½ teaspoons	2 teaspoons
lemon extract	½ teaspoon	¾ teaspoon	1 teaspoon
stevia	10 drops	15 drops	20 drops

BLUEBERRY CUSTARD

You need:
double boiler
wire whisk
spatula
measuring cups
measuring spoons

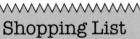

Shopping List

low fat milk
whole eggs
egg whites
blueberries
fructose
cream
strawberry essence
vanilla extract
mint leaves
stevia

 ½ cup low fat milk

 1 whole egg
¼ cup egg white

 ¼ cup blueberries
1 tablespoon fructose

 ½ cup cream

 PLUS! ¼ teaspoon strawberry essence
½ teaspoon vanilla extract
2 mint leaves
5 drops stevia ✿

 1 In the top of a double boiler (or a non-stick sauce pan), whisk together the egg, egg whites, stevia, and cream.

 2 Continue to whisk slowly until the mixture starts to thicken and steam. Whisk continuously for one minute more.

 3 Remove from the heat, whisk in the strawberry essence, vanilla extract and fructose. Pour into two custard cups.

 4 Chill one hour. Top with chopped fruit to serve.

 For variations of flavors use different fruits:
½ cup raspberries, or
½ cup peaches, or
½ cup strawberries, or
½ cup blackberries

✪ To find the stevia supplement, see page 200.

SHARE THIS MEAL WITH FRIENDS AND FAMILY.

Ingredients			
low fat milk	1 cup	1½ cups	2 cups
whole eggs	2	3	4
egg whites	½ cup	¾ cup	1 cup
blueberries	½ cup	¾ cup	1 cup
fructose	⅛ cup	3 tablespoons	¼ cup
cream	1 cup	1½ cups	2 cups
strawberry essence	½ teaspoon	¾ teaspoon	1 teaspoon
vanilla extract	1 teaspoon	1½ teaspoons	2 teaspoons
mint leaves	4	6	8
stevia	10 drops	15 drops	20 drops
raspberries OR	1 cup	1½ cups	2 cups
peaches OR	1 cup	1½ cups	2 cups
strawberries OR	1 cup	1½ cups	2 cups
blackberries	1 cup	1½ cups	2 cups

MIGHTY SWEET POTATO PIE

You need:
medium mixing bowl
potato peeler
spatula
sauce pan
measuring cups & spoons
electric mixer
pie pan

Shopping List

low fat buttermilk
eggs
whey protein powder
sweet potatoes
fructose
unsweetened applesauce
pecans
butter
extra-light olive oil
ginger
vanilla extract
lemon essence
pumpkin pie spice
nutmeg
salt

 1 cup low fat buttermilk

 4 eggs
1 cup whey protein powder

 3 medium mashed sweet potatoes
3/4 cup fructose
3/4 cup unsweetened applesauce

 1/2 cup chopped pecans
5 tablespoons butter
1/2 cup extra-light olive oil

 1/2 teaspoon ginger
PLUS! 1 tablespoon vanilla extract
1 teaspoon lemon essence
1 teaspoon pumpkin pie spice
2 teaspoons nutmeg
1/2 teaspoon salt

EASY! OUCH! HOT!

 1   Pre heat the oven to 450°F. Chop the pecans and set aside.

 2   Peel, steam and mash sweet potatoes, set aside. Blend the butter, and fructose with an electric mixer.

 3   Slowly blend in the sweet potatoes, olive oil, applesauce, eggs (one at a time), low fat buttermilk, and whey protein powder.

 4   Add the ginger, vanilla extract, lemon essence, pumpkin pie spice, nutmeg, and salt.

 5   Pour into an almond or Brazil nut crust and sprinkle with chopped pecans.

 6   Bake at 450°F for ten minutes, then 350°F for another hour.

SHARE THIS MEAL WITH FRIENDS AND FAMILY

Ingredients			
low fat buttermilk	2 cups	3 cups	4 cups
eggs	8	12	16
whey protein powder	2 cups	3 cups	4 cups
sweet potatoes	6	9	12
fructose	1½ cups	2¼ cups	3 cups
unsweetened applesauce	1½ cups	2¼ cups	3 cups
chopped pecans	1 cup	1½ cups	2 cups
butter	10 tablespoons	15 tablespoons	20 tablespoons
extra-light olive oil	1 cup	1½ cups	2 cups
ginger	1 teaspoon	1½ teaspoons	2 teaspoons
vanilla extract	⅛ cup	3 tablespoons	¼ cup
lemon essence	2 teaspoons	1 tablespoon	4 teaspoons
pumpkin pie spice	2 teaspoons	1 tablespoon	4 teaspoons
nutmeg	4 teaspoons	⅛ cup	8 teaspoons
salt	1 teaspoon	1½ teaspoons	2 teaspoons

PEACH COBBLER

PREP TIME: 15 MINUTES
COOK TIME: 10 MINUTES

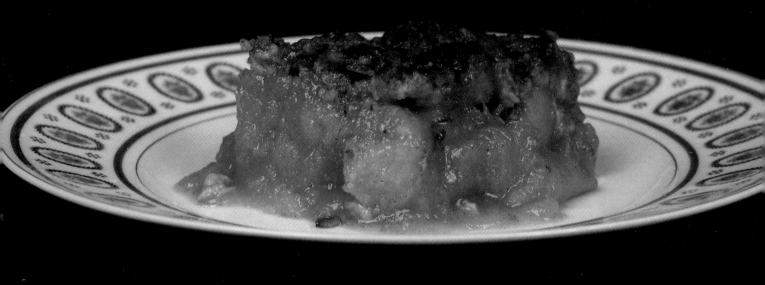

You need:
medium bowl
spatula
broiler-safe pan
measuring cups
measuring spoons

Shopping List
Knox unflavored gelatin
whey protein powder
fresh or frozen peaches
fructose
unsweetened applesauce
slow cooking oats
butter
extra-light olive oil
vanilla extract
cinnamon
nutmeg
stevia

1 envelope Knox unflavored gelatin
1/2 cup whey protein powder

8 cups sliced fresh or frozen peaches
1 cup fructose
1 cup unsweetened applesauce
1 cup slow cooking oats

1/4 cup butter
1/4 cup extra-light olive oil

PLUS!
1 teaspoon vanilla extract
1 tablespoon cinnamon
1 teaspoon nutmeg
10 drops stevia✪

✪ To find the stevia supplement, see page 200.

EASY! OUCH! HOT!

 1 In a medium bowl, mix the vanilla, stevia and applesauce. Add the gelatin and let sit.

 2 Slice the peaches and cook with the fructose on the stove top for 8-10 minutes, until soft. Remove from the heat.

 3 Add the applesauce mixture.

 4 Pour into a broiler-safe pan (not glass).

 5 Mix together the protein powder, rolled oats, cinnamon, nutmeg, butter and oil with a fork or crumble together with your fingers and sprinkle over the fruit.

 6 Put under broiler to brown the topping. Cool before serving.

SHARE THIS MEAL WITH FRIENDS AND FAMILY

Ingredients			
Knox unflavored gelatin	2 envelopes	3 envelopes	4 envelopes
whey protein powder	1 cup	1½ cups	2 cups
peaches	16 cups	24 cups	32 cups
fructose	2 cups	3 cups	4 cups
unsweetened applesauce	2 cups	3 cups	4 cups
slow cooking oats	2 cups	3 cups	4 cups
butter	½ cup	¾ cup	1 cup
extra-light olive oil	½ cup	¾ cup	1 cup
vanilla extract	2 teaspoons	1 tablespoon	4 teaspoons
cinnamon	⅛ cup	3 tablespoons	¼ cup
nutmeg	2 teaspoons	1 tablespoon	4 teaspoons
stevia	15 drops	20 drops	25 drops

FRUITY GELLO SNACK

PREP TIME: 15 MINUTES
COOK TIME: 10 MINUTES

You need:
dessert dishes
small sharp knife
spatula
sauce pan
measuring cups
measuring spoons

Shopping List
Knox unflavored gelatin
kiwis
raspberries
strawberries
red seedless grapes
chopped walnuts
whipping cream
spring water
banana extract
orange extract
strawberry extract
mint leaves
stevia

4 envelopes Knox unflavored gelatin

1 kiwi, peeled and diced
1 cup raspberries
1 cup strawberries, diced
1/3 cup red seedless grapes, halved

4 teaspoons chopped walnuts
1/4 cup whipped cream

PLUS!

2 cups spring water
1 tablespoon banana extract☺☺
1 tablespoon orange extract☺☺
1/2 teaspoon strawberry extract☺☺
4 mint leaves
5 drops stevia☺

☺ To find the stevia supplement, see page 200.
☺☺ These extracts are found in health food stores.

 1 Place gelatin, stevia, and water in a saucepan, stir until dissolved, then add fruit and extracts.

 2 Heat to a simmer, stirring gently for 10 minutes until the raspberries dissolve.

 3 Put one teaspoon of chopped walnuts in each dish. Pour the liquid into dessert dishes and let cool.

 4 When fruit salad has set, garnish with mint leaves. For a special treat, top each dish with a tablespoon of fresh whipped cream.❂

 *When choosing berries, look for those that are medium-sized and uniform in color. They should be solid to the touch and not leaking juice.*

 To make whipped cream: In a chilled bowl combine 1 cup whipping cream, 2 tablespoons powdered sugar and ½ teaspoon vanilla extract. Beat with an electric beater on medium speed until soft peaks form. Serve on each dessert.

SHARE THIS MEAL WITH FRIENDS AND FAMILY

Ingredients			
Knox gelatin	8 envelopes	12 envelopes	16 envelopes
Kiwis	2	3	4
raspberries	2 cups	3 cups	4 cups
strawberries	2 cups	3 cups	4 cups
red seedless grapes	⅔ cup	1 cup	1⅓ cups
chopped walnuts	8 teaspoons	4 tablespoons	16 teaspoons
whipped cream	½ cup	¾ cup	1 cup
spring water	1 quart	1½ quarts	2 quarts
banana extract	⅛ cup	3 tablespoons	¼ cup
orange extract	⅛ cup	3 tablespoons	¼ cup
strawberry extract	1 teaspoon	1½ teaspoons	2 teaspoons
mint leaves	8	12	16
stevia	10 drops	15 drops	20 drops

WEEKEND TREATS—WHAT ARE YOU EATING?

Sweets are a wonderful treat to enjoy if we balance them. By keeping insulin stable, we can enjoy our meal with a balanced dessert. If you go out to a restaurant, just order a protein entreé and a salad. Skip the potatoes, pasta, bread and vegetables and enjoy ⅓ of the dessert. When you eat balanced you never feel deprived.

Angel Food Cake	1 Piece	*7 sugar cubes
Protein 2 Grams		
Carbohydrates 16 Grams		
Sugar 7 Cubes		
Glycemic Index 99		
Glycemic Load 99 x 16/100=16		
Effective Sugar Cube Load-7		
Sodium (each=50mg) 210 mg		

Chocolate Cake	1/8 of 18 ounce cake	*8 sugar cubes
Protein 3 Grams		
Carbohydrates 33 Grams		
Sugar 14 Cubes		
Glycemic Index 54		
Glycemic Load 54 x 33/100=18		
Effective Sugar Cube Load-8		
Total Fat 11 Grams		
Monounsaturated Fat-6 Grams		
Saturated Fat-3 Grams		
Sodium (each=50mg) 214 mg		

By themselves, these desserts may not look too bad. Remember to check what the rest of the meal contains!

Corn Muffin — 1 — *42 sugar cubes

Nutrient															
Protein 8 Grams															
Carbohydrates 66 Grams															
Sugar 29 Cubes															
Glycemic Index 146															
Glycemic Load 146 x 50/100=73															
Effective Sugar Cube Load-42															
Total Fat 14 Grams															
Monounsaturated Fat-4 Grams															
Saturated Fat-2 Grams															
Sodium (each=50mg) 875 mg															

Pop Tart, Cherry — 1 pop tart — *19 sugar cubes

Nutrient															
Protein 3 Grams															
Carbohydrates 36 Grams															
Sugar 16 Cubes															
Glycemic Index 100															
Glycemic Load 100 x 37/100=37															
Effective Sugar Cube Load-16															
Total Fat 5 Grams															
Monounsaturated Fat-3 Grams															
Saturated Fat-1 Grams															
Sodium (each=50mg) 203 mg															

GLOSSARY

This section explains some of the terms used in the book:

MEASURING LIQUID INGREDIENTS

Most liquid measuring cups are see-through and have a spout for pouring. To get an accurate measurement, put the cup on the counter and make sure you bring the liquid to the exact line you need. If you are measuring something sticky such as nut butter, put a little oil in the cup before you add the nut butter and it will slide out easily.

MEASURING DRY INGREDIENTS

Most dry measuring cups are stackable. Find the cup size you need and fill to the top. Don't shake or pack it in to get more, because it will present a problem for your recipe. Using the flat edge of a table knife, scrape across the top so you have a level measurement. When you measure chopped nuts or shredded cheese, spoon the ingredients into the cup until they reach the top. Don't press down.

ZEST

The outermost part of the rind of citrus fruits such as lemons or oranges can be used as flavoring. To do this, use a fine grater or a cooking instrument called a zester, a small tool with five tiny round blades at the end. When it is dragged across an orange or lemon, it removes long thin shreds of rind that can be used in a recipe or as a garnish.

STEVIA

Stevia is an herb that is 200 to 300 times sweeter than regular sugar, has no calories, is suitable for diabetics, is safe for children, does not cause cavities, and is heat stable, so it can be used for cooking and baking. It has been used widely and safely consumed in many countries around the world for decades. Stevia is an herb derived from a plant of the daisy family that grows in South America. In 1995 the FDA allowed stevia to be used as a dietary supplement. Only a small amount of the supplement is needed to enhance flavors in a recipe. If you are using liquid stevia, use 5 drops per serving. For more information go to www.stevia.com. The best source of stevia we have found is Astraya and can be purchased from www.celtic-seasalt.com or call 800-867-7258.

GLYCEMIC INDEX

The glycemic index ranks foods according to their ability to raise blood sugar levels. This great breakthrough over the last 25 years has given us a great insight into understanding how foods affect us. It is based on scientifically confirmed nutritional information. Research has shown that lower glycemic index foods:

⭐ Reduce the risk of heart disease, obesity and Type II diabetes.

⭐ Give us measurable ways to control insulin levels, helping our bodies burn fat more readily.

⭐ Help lower blood fats.

⭐ Give us measurable ways to control blood sugar levels.

⭐ Help keep us from overeating.

The glycemic index ranks foods based on their immediate effect on blood sugar levels. It was first developed in 1981 by a team of scientists led by Dr. David Jenkins, a professor at the University of

Toronto, Canada to help determine which foods were best for people with diabetes. Carbohydrates stimulate the secretion of insulin. Slow absorption of carbohydrates means that the pancreas doesn't have to work hard, thereby secreting less insulin. If the pancreas is overstimulated for a long time it may become exhausted and lead to Type II diabetes. Research has shown that high insulin levels are one of the key factors in the development of heart disease and hypertension. As insulin influences how we metabolize our foods, it determines whether we burn fat or carbohydrates to meet our energy needs, thereby determining if we store fat in our bodies. The higher the glycemic index, the more health problems we may incur. The glycemic index has became the definitive guideline to determine which carbohydrates to eat.

GLYCEMIC LOAD

To determine the glycemic index, it requires that one consumes around 50 grams of carbohydrate. It would be extremely difficult to eat this quantity of vegetables at one sitting—about 16 cups of steamed broccoli. Therefore, nearly all glycemic index work has been done with grains, starches, and some fruits. Almost nothing is known about the glycemic index of low-density vegetables that are vital for a balanced diet.

These difficulties have led to a more specific process called the glycemic load, which is far more significant than the glycemic index in determining the insulin output of a meal. The glycemic load is the actual amount of insulin-stimulating carbohydrate consumed multiplied by the glycemic index of the specific food. A small volume of high-glycemic carbohydrate has the same effect on insulin as a large volume of low-glycemic carbohydrate. This shows that eating too many low-glycemic carbohydrates can have a major effect on increased insulin production. For example, black beans have a low-glycemic index because of their high fiber content. However, they are also very dense in carbohydrate content. As a result, eating too many black beans at a meal can profoundly stimulate insulin production.

A balanced diet is best achieved by consuming low-density carbohydrates that have a low-glycemic index. That means eating a lot of vegetables. The glycemic load is determined by multiplying the number of grams of insulin-stimulating carbohydrate times the glycemic index for that carbohydrate. The lower the glycemic load number, the lower the insulin stimulation of that carbohydrate.

For example:

Item	Amount	CHO Grams	Glycemic Index	Glycemic Load	Sugar Cubes
Apple	1	19	40	760	3
Apple Juice	1 cup	29	57	1653	7
Orange	1 medium	15	75	1125	5
Orange Juice	1 cup	26	85	2210	10
4 oz. Bagel	1	58	139	8062	36
White Bread	1 slice	15	100	1500	7
Wheat Bread	1 slice	13	89	1157	5
Macaroni & Cheese	2 cups	68	64	4352	19
Cheerios	1 serving*	59	111	6549	25
Baked Potato	1 large	57	158	9006	39
White Rice	1 cup	53	96	5088	22
Watermelon	1 wedge	22	103	2266	10
Pinto beans	1 cup	29	67	1943	8
Chocolate Milk	1 cup	24	70	1680	7

*1 serving usually equals 3 cups or more

To maintain good health, a meal should not contain a glycemic load of more than 3,000 units at any one time. From the examples on the chart on page 201, eating grains or juices give a meal a very high glycemic load and results in a high insulin response. Fruits are far better than juices. We have made a number of charts for you to check your diet to make sure you are not eating foods with a high glycemic load. New research constantly updates these charts. Resources for information on the glycemic index and glycemic load are:

www.glycemicindex.com A glycemic index program launched in Australia and New Zealand. Glycemic Index is based on glucose.

American Journal of Clinical Nutrition **2002;76:5-56** The International table of glycemic index and glycemic load values: 2002, based on white bread and glucose.

SPECIAL FLOUR PRODUCTS

Check your local health food store for garbanzo flour, lentil flour and nut flours. If they are not available, other good sources are Bob's Red Mill, www.bobsredmill.com; Arrowhead Mills, www.arrowheadmills.com; King Arthur Flour, www.kingarthurflour.com; and Hodgson Mill Flour, www.hodgsonmill.com.

FATTY ACID ANALYSIS
www.yourfuturehealth.com

To check your fatty acid levels check with your physician or call toll free 877-468-6934. Your Future Health will help you obtain the kit and find a resource to draw the blood.

INFORMATIVE WEB SITES
www.kidsneedusnow.org

Kids Need Us Now is an informative site for children and adults relating to information about ADD, ADHD, and dyslexia. This site not only gives information, it gives many action steps to overcome these problems. KIDS is dedicated to children of all ages, and was created to provide opportunities for each to be proud of his or her learning style and creative difference.

www.hellofriend.org

The Hello Friend Foundation is a public, non-profit organization dedicated to those with learning differences and helps those with creative needs to celebrate their individual creativity. The Foundation promotes the early recognition of differences, compassionate understanding, and thereby encourages effective education. The site has numerous resources and projects that are ongoing.

www.amenclinic.com

The Amen Clinic for Behavioral Medicine is an innovative clinic specializing in uniquely thorough diagnostic methodologies for a wide variety of neuropsychiatric, behavioral and learning problems for children. The Amen Clinic is well known for its creative work with brain SPECT imaging. Dr. Amen has written some of the finest books available about ADD, ADHD and other learning differences. His in-depth research has opened the door for many to finally understand why they are suffering when there is so little understood about what is happening.

www.drsears.com

The Zone is not some mystical place. It is a state of hormonal balance that can be achieved by your diet. In particular, it can be defined as keeping the hormone insulin in a tight zone: not too high, not too low. The Zone Diet is a lifelong hormonal control strategy. Once you begin to think about food hormonally instead of calorically, you begin to realize that many of the dietary recommendations made by the U.S. government and leading nutritional experts are simply wrong.

www.covd.org

Functional Optometry recognizes the following facts:

- Visual differences can and often do interfere with learning.

- Learning related visual problems need the expertise of a functional optometrist who does a through diagnostic and management service.

- The goal of the functional optometrist is to improve visual function and relieve interfering symptoms.

- Prompt diagnosis and proper therapy enhance the ability to learn to one's full potential.

Those with learning differences require help from many disciplines and functional optometry contributes one aspect of the multidisciplinary management required for lifelong learning.

www.uoguelph.ca/~bholub/

Dr. Bruce Holub is one of the leading researchers regarding EPA and the use of fatty acids. His work is focused upon human-based research trials wherein various dietary fatty acid components (Omega-3 fatty acids from fish/fish oils, etc.) plus selected nutraceutical/functional foods are evaluated with respect to their potential to favorably influence a whole range of risk factors for CVD. The risk factors of interest are those which are currently measured in the public health care system (e.g. LDL cholesterol, HDL cholesterol, triglyceride, etc.) as well as those which are not available currently in the health care system. The latter include various thrombogenic, atherogenic, inflammatory, and other risk factors. The potential impact of modifying dietary constituents ranging from lipid/fatty acids through to phytonutraceuticals on these conventional and non-conventional risk factors are under current investigation. His research group has also developed particular interest in sectors within the population, including males and females of varying ages, ethnic backgrounds, stages of life (e.g. post-menopausal women on or not on hormone-replacement therapy, etc.) since there is evidence now that genetic and other factors can influence the responsiveness of individuals to given nutritional interventions. In addition, he is also extensively involved in collaborative epidemiological work with groups within North America (including medical centers and health agencies in Canada and the U. S.) as well as international groups (in Greenland).

www.nutrasource.ca

Nutrasource Diagnostics Inc., a University of Guelph spin-off company, is the world leader in Omega-3 diagnostic care, nutraceutical and functional food certification, and clinical trials relating to the nutraceutical and functional food industry. Through the Human Nutraceutical Research Unit at the University of Guelph, NDI offers clinical validation in the areas of essential fatty acid testing, bioavailability, product analysis, and measurable health benefit. In addition, NDI offers its unique I.F.O.S. program (International Fish Oil Standards) providing the consumer with clean and credible sources of Omega-3 enriched products. Physicians can contact the lab at 519-824-4120 x 58817 to receive information about the fatty acid analysis, including research studies regarding the tests, and to order blood test kits.

REFERENCES

WEB SITES

www.glycemicindex.com A glycemic index program launched in Australia and New Zealand. Glycemic Index is based on glucose.

American Journal of Clinical Nutrition 2002;76:5-56 The International table of glycemic index and glycemic load values: 2002. Glycemic Index is based on white bread and glucose.

The USDA National Nutrient Database for Standard Reference. An internet site that evaluates different foods for their nutritional content.**www.nal.usda.gov/fnic/cgi-bin/nut_search.pl.**

BOOKS

Sears, Barry, Bill Lawren. 1995. *The Zone: A Dietary Road Map to Lose Weight Permanently: Reset Your Genetic Code: Prevent Disease: Achieve Maximum Physical Performance.*

Sears, Barry. 2000. *A Week in the Zone.*

Sears, Barry, Mary Goodbody. 1996. *Mastering the Zone: The Next Step in Achieving SuperHealth and Permanent Fat Loss.*

Sears, Barry. 2002. *The Omega Rx Zone: The Miracle of the New High-Dose Fish Oil.*

Sears, Barry.. 2001. *The Soy Zone: 101 Delicious and Easy-to-Prepare Recipes.*

Amen, Daniel G. 2002. *Healing ADD.*

Amen, Daniel G. 2000. *Change Your Brain, Change Your Life.*

Amen, Daniel G. 2002. *Healing The Hardware Of The Soul.*

Netzer, Corinne T. 2003. *The Complete Book of Food Counts - 6th Edition.*

PUBLICATIONS

Wolever TM, Mehling C. Long-term effect of varying the source or amount of dietary carbohydrate on postprandial plasma glucose, insulin, triacylglycerol, and free fatty acid concentrations in subjects with impaired glucose tolerance. *Am J Clin Nutr.* 2003 Mar;77(3) 612-621.

Rizkalla SW, Bellisle F, Slama G. Health benefits of low glycemic index foods, such as pulses, in diabetic patients and healthy individuals. *Br J Nutr.* 2002 Dec;88 Suppl 3:S255-62.

Heacock PM, Hertzler SR, Wolf BW. Fructose prefeeding reduces the glycemic response to a high-glycemic index, starchy food in humans. *J Nutr.* 2002 Sep;132(9):2601-4.

Brand-Miller JC, Holt SH, Pawlak DB, McMillan J. Glycemic index and obesity. *Am J Clin Nutr.* 2002 Jul;76(1):281S-5S.

Jenkins DJ, Kendall CW, Augustin LS, Franceschi S, Hamidi M, Marchie A, Jenkins AL, Axelsen M. Glycemic index: overview of implications in health and disease. *Am J Clin Nutr.* 2002 Jul;76(1):266S-73S.

Ludwig DS, Eckel RH.The glycemic index at 20 y. *Am J Clin Nutr.* 2002 Jul;76(1):264S-5S.

Foster-Powell K, Holt SH, Brand-Miller JC. International table of glycemic index and glycemic load values: 2002. *Am J Clin Nutr.* 2002 Jul;76(1):5-56.

Ostman EM, Liljeberg Elmstahl HG, Bjorck IM. Barley bread containing lactic acid improves glucose tolerance at a subsequent meal in healthy men and women. *J Nutr.* 2002 Jun;132(6):1173-5.

Ludwig DS. The glycemic index: physiological mechanisms relating to obesity, diabetes, and cardiovascular disease. *JAMA*. 2002 May 8;287(18):2414-23.

Ebbeling CB, Ludwig DS. Treating obesity in youth: should dietary glycemic load be a consideration? *Adv Pediatr*. 2001;48:179-212.

Gilbertson HR, Brand-Miller JC, Thorburn AW, Evans S, Chondros P, Werther GA. The effect of flexible low glycemic index dietary advice versus measured carbohydrate exchange diets on glycemic control in children with type 1 diabetes. *Diabetes Care*. 2001 Jul;24(7):1137-43.

Spieth LE, Harnish JD, Lenders CM, Raezer LB, Pereira MA, Hangen SJ, Ludwig DS. A low-glycemic index diet in the treatment of pediatric obesity. *Arch Pediatr Adolesc Med*. 2000 Sep;154(9):947-51.

Wolever TM, Mehling C. Long-term effect of varying the source or amount of dietary carbohydrate on postprandial plasma glucose, insulin, triacylglycerol, and free fatty acid concentrations in subjects with impaired glucose tolerance. *Am J Clin Nutr*. 2003 Mar;77(3):612-621.

Wolever TM. Low carbohydrate does not mean low glycemic index! *Br J Nutr*. 2002 Aug;88(2):211-2; author reply 213-4.

Wolever TM. American Diabetes Association evidence-based nutrition principles and recommendations are not based on evidence. *Diabetes Care*. 2002 Jul;25(7):1263-4; author reply 1264-5.

Wolever TM, Mehling C. High-carbohydrate-low-glycaemic index dietary advice improves glucose disposition index in subjects with impaired glucose tolerance. *Br J Nutr*. 2002 May;87(5):477-87.

Recommendations for the nutritional management of patients with diabetes mellitus. *European Journal of Clinical Nutrition* (2000) 54, 353±355 ß 2000.

Glycaemic index of foods: a little empiricism among the dogma of diabetic diets.

Dietitians Association of Australia review paper. Glycaemic index in diabetes management. *Br J Nutr* 2002 Dec;88 Suppl 3:S255-62.

Health benefits of low glycemic index foods, such as pulses, in diabetic patients and healthy individuals. Rizkalla SW, Bellisle F, Slama G. Department of Diabetes, *INSERM* U341 and Assistance Publique, Hotel-Dieu, 1, Place du Parvis Notre-Dame, 75004 Paris, France. J Nutr 2002 Sep;132(9):2601-4.

Voigt RG, Llorente AM, Jensen CL, Fraley JK, Berretta MC, Heird WC. A randomized, double-blind, placebo-controlled trial of docosahexaenoic acid supplementation in children with attention-deficit/hyperactivity disorder. *J Pediatr*. 2001 Aug;139(2):189-96.

Burgess JR, Stevens L, Zhang W, Peck L. Long-chain polyunsaturated fatty acids in children with attention-deficit hyperactivity disorder. *Am J Clin Nutr*. 2000 Jan;71(1 Suppl):327S-30S.

Mitchell EA, Aman MG, Turbott SH, Manku M. Clinical characteristics and serum essential fatty acid levels in hyperactive children. *Clin Pediatr* (Phila). 1987 Aug;26(8):406-11.

Schwartz MB, Puhl R. Childhood obesity: a societal problem to solve. *Obes Rev*. 2003 Feb;4(1):57-71.

Berg F, Buechner J, Parham E. Guidelines for childhood obesity prevention programs: promoting healthy weight in children. *J Nutr Educ Behav*. 2003 Jan-Feb;35(1):1-4.

Davis SP, Davis M, Northington L, Moll G, Kolar K. Childhood obesity reduction by school based programs. *ABNF J*. 2002 Nov-Dec;13(6):145-9.

Massiera F, Saint-Marc P, Seydoux J, Murata T, Kobayashi T, Narumiya S, Guesnet P, Amri EZ, Negrel R, Ailhaud G,. Arachidonic acid and prostacyclin signaling promote adipose tissue development: a human health concern? *J Lipid Res*. 2003 Feb;44(2):271-9.

Sievenpiper JL, Jenkins AL, Whitham DL, Vuksan V. Insulin resistance: concepts, controversies, and the role of nutrition. *Can J Diet Pract Res.* 2002 Spring;63(1):20-32.

Ludwig DS. Dietary glycemic index and obesity. *J Nutr.* 2000 Feb;130(2S Suppl):280S-283S.

Ludwig DS, Majzoub JA, Al-Zahrani A, Dallal GE, Blanco I, Roberts SB. High glycemic index foods, overeating, and obesity. *Pediatrics.* 1999 Mar;103(3):E26.

Augustin LS, Polesel J, Bosetti C, Kendall CW, La Vecchia C, Parpinel M, Conti E, Montella M, Franceschi S, Jenkins DJ, Dal Maso L. Dietary glycemic index, glycemic load and ovarian cancer risk: a case-control study in Italy. *Ann Oncol.* 2003 Jan;14(1):78-84.

Liu S, Willett WC. Dietary glycemic load and atherothrombotic risk. *Curr Atheroscler Rep.* 2002 Nov;4(6):454-61.

Willett W, Manson J, Liu S. Glycemic index, glycemic load, and risk of type 2 diabetes. *Am J Clin Nutr.* 2002 Jul;76(1):274S-80S.

Brink PJ. The glycemic load. West *J Nurs Res.* 2001 Aug;23(5):437-40. Review.

B.J. Holub. Clinical nutrition:4. Omega-3 fatty acids in cardiovascular care. *CMAJ* 166:608-15 (2002).

E. Dewailly, C. Blanchet, S. Gingras, S. Lemieux, L. Sauve, J. Bergeron, B. Holub. Relations between n-3 fatty acid status and cardiovascular disease risk factors among Quebecers. *AJCN* 74:603-11 (2001).

E. Dewailly, C. Blanchet, S. Lemieux, L. Sauve, S. Gingras, P. Ayotte, Holub. n-3 Fatty acids and cardiovascular disease risk factors among the Inuit of Nunavik. *AJCN* 74:464-73 (2001).

C. Blanchet, E. Dewailly, P. Ayotte, S. Bruneau, O. Receveur, B. Holub. Contribution of Selected Traditional and Market Foods to the Diet of Nunavik Inuit Women. *Can J Diet Pract Res* 61:50-59 (2000).

K. Stark, E. Park, V. Maines and B. Holub. Effect of a fish-oil concentrate on serum lipids in postmenopausal women receiving and not receiving hormone replacement therapy in a placebo-controlled, double-blind trial. *AJCN* 72:389-94 (2000) Paper.

Conquer, J.A.,Tierney, M.C., Zecevic, J., Bettger, W.J. and Fisher, R.H. 2000. Fatty acid analysis of blood plasma of patients with Alzheimer's disease, other types of dementia, and cognitive impairment. *Lipids* 35: 1505-1512.

B. Holub. Hydrogenated fats and serum cholesterol levels. *NEJM* 341(18):1396 (1999).

A. Adler and B. Holub. Effect of garlic and fish oil supplementation on serum lipid and lipoprotein concentrations in hypercholesterolemic men. *AJCN* 65:445-450 (1997) Abstract.

J. Conquer and B. Holub. Supplementation with an algae source of docosahexaenoic acid increases n-3 fatty acid status and alters selected risk factors for heart disease in vegetarian subjects. *J. Nutr.* 126:3032-3039 (1996).

ILLUSTRATIONS

The illustration information was extracted from the following sources: www.nal.usda.gov/fnic/foodcomp, 2002, Netzer, Corinne T. 2003. *The complete Book of Food Counts* and www.nal.usda.gov/fnic/foodcomp, The USDA Nutrient Data Laboratory.

Food Recommendations

Recommended bread
Men's Bread
Women's Bread
www.frenchmeadow.com

Recommended Extra-Light Olive Oil

Bertolli
Filippo Berio
DaVinc

Fruit2O
www.fruit20.com

Recommended Flour

Bob's Red Mill
www.bobsredmill.com

Arrowhead Mills
www.arrowheadmills.com

King Arthur Flour
www.kingarthurflour.com

Hodgson Mill Flour
www.hodgsonmill.com

BIOGRAPHY

René Thomas, M.A., D.C., N.D.

Through her extensive writings, lectures, research and clinical experience, Dr. René is internationally regarded as one of the most innovative and forward-thinking practitioners in her field—the treatment of disorders through a greater understanding of the body's complex neurological systems. Her work, a part of which is known as Body Integration, has achieved widespread acclaim in the treatment of muscular dystrophy, MS, and various immune system related diseases, plus therapies that have achieved dramatic results for children with learning differences. She is the author of more than seventy diagnostic and therapeutic manuals in wide use by chiropractors and naturopathic physicians worldwide.

As part of this work, Dr. René has dedicated over three decades to help children with Attention Deficit Hyperactivity Disorder and Dyslexia. The program described in *Powerful Foods For Powerful Minds and Bodies* makes accessible to children and parents her vast research and experience working with the relationship of neurological function and diet. This has been highlighted by her collaboration with Dr. Barry Sears, whereby her neurological data when, combined with the Zone diet and intake of high dose pharmaceutical grade fish oil, created dramatic results. This program has formed the basis of two organizations to assist parents and children who choose to take pro-active steps to improve their lives. Dr. René formed the non-profit Adopt A Patient Foundation and the for-profit Kids Need Us Now, LLC. In addition to her Nature's Mighty Bites™ food products, and Nature's Mighty 3s™ microencapsulated fish oil, Dr. René's new book brings great promise in restoring hope by helping all children improve their performance in school and have healthier and happier lives.

Dr. René is based in Woburn, Massachusetts, where she serves as the Executive Director of the New Hope Center. She holds doctoral degrees in chiropractic plus masters and bachelor degrees.

Jennifer Smith worked as an art director before starting her own design firm. As her family grew, she transitioned from design to teaching others how to use computers for graphic design and founded AGI training. Jennifer is an Adobe Certified trainer who lives and works in the Boston area. She enjoys cooking and spending time with her children.

INDEX

A

AA. *See* Arachidonic acid

ADD 4, 11, 12, 13, 25, 34, 38, 46, 48, 50, 51, 52, 54, 55, 56, 58, 60, 66, 67, 68, 69, 70, 71, 72, 73, 74, 75, 76, 77, 79, 81, 82, 84, 86, 88, 90, 92, 94, 96, 98, 100, 102, 104, 106, 108, 110, 117, 118, 120, 122, 124, 126, 128, 130, 132, 134, 136, 138, 140, 142, 144, 146, 148, 150, 152, 156, 157, 158, 159, 160, 161, 162, 163, 164, 165, 166, 167, 168. 169, 175, 176, 179, 180, 182, 184, 186, 188, 189, 190, 192, 194, 196

ADHD 4, 11, 12, 13, 25, 34

allspice 184

almonds 33, 50, 51, 52, 53, 54, 56, 57, 65, 66, 80, 81, 94, 95, 98, 99, 100, 101, 136, 158, 161, 165, 175, 179, 184, 186, 188, 189

Amen, Daniel 11

apple 55, 94, 96, 164, 166
  applesauce 30, 58, 59, 60, 61, 62, 110, 176, 180, 189, 192, 194

Arachidonic acid 13

avocado 106, 107, 168

B

bacon 28, 52, 53, 56, 57, 158

baking powder 58, 84, 176, 180

baking soda 60, 176

banana 63, 67, 69, 70, 71, 74, 162

banana extract 196

barley 58, 59, 60, 61, 84, 176

basil 122, 123, 152, 153

beans 108

beef 108, 118, 150, 152, 168
  beef stock 152

blackberries 75

black pepper 48

blueberries 58, 59, 60, 61, 62, 63, 71, 75, 92, 93, 169, 190

Brazil nuts 175

bread 31, 56, 57, 160

broccoli 27, 30, 82, 83, 98, 99, 146, 148

butter 33, 55, 67, 70, 79, 81, 126, 127, 156, 161, 162, 164, 166, 186, 192, 194

buttermilk 58, 59, 60, 61, 176, 180, 192

C

cantaloupe 46, 47, 51, 92, 158

carbohydrates 9, 11, 21, 25, 26, 27, 28, 31, 32, 35, 36

carrot 80, 98, 99, 124, 130, 134, 152

cashews 33, 48, 49, 65

celery 102, 103, 132, 134, 136, 138

cereals 31

cheese 29, 33, 46, 47, 48, 49, 51, 54, 88, 160, 167
  cheddar cheese 96, 106, 108, 126, 168, 169
  cream cheese 130
  mozzarella cheese 86
  parmesan cheese 86
  string cheese 94

cherries 76, 82

chicken 28, 33, 40, 79, 82, 83, 86, 87, 100, 101, 102, 103, 104, 105, 117, 134, 136, 140, 144, 146, 150

chili powder 106, 108

chives 48, 49

cinnamon 52, 53, 58, 59, 60, 61, 62, 81, 96, 161, 176, 189, 194

cocoa 157, 182, 188

coconut 79, 140, 142, 186

coriander 122, 123

corn 180

corn meal 144, 180

corn starch 152

Cosby, Bill 4

Cosby, Camille O. 4, 9

cottage cheese 51

cream 32, 33, 104, 105, 110, 111, 190

cucumber 80, 100, 101, 124, 130, 144

D

dairy 29

depression 11

DHA 12, 13, 37, 38

dill 100, 101, 130, 131

dyslexia 12

E

egg 29, 31, 46, 47, 48, 49, 56, 57, 58, 59, 60, 61, 163, 190, 192

egg white 84, 88, 92, 110, 128, 132, 144, 175, 176, 179, 180,

184, 186, 188, 190

elbow macaroni 126

EPA 11, 12, 13, 29, 37, 38

F

fat 7, 10, 11, 17, 22, 25, 26, 27, 28, 29, 33, 34, 35, 36, 37

fatty acid 10, 12

fat chart 33

fish 11, 12, 29, 33, 37, 38, 138, 139

fish oil 37

flaxseed oil 38

fructose 117, 118, 119, 120, 121, 124, 125, 175, 176, 179, 184, 186, 188, 190, 192, 194

fruits 30, 31

fruit juices 31

G

garbanzo 128, 129

garlic 106, 107, 108, 109, 117, 118, 152

gelatin 184, 189, 194, 196

ginger 79, 184, 192

Glycemic
  Index 25
  Load 25

grains 31

grapefruit 46

grapes 48, 49, 50, 54, 100, 118, 196

guacamole 33, 106, 107, 168

H

ham 86, 87

Holub, Bruce 11

honeydew 100, 101, 158

hummus 132, 133, 163

I

insulin 10, 25, 32, 34, 35, 36, 37

K

kale 104, 105

kiwi 77, 102, 196

L

label 26

lemon 70, 74, 79, 80, 82, 83, 100, 101, 130, 144, 146, 148, 192

lemon extract 189

lemon herb seasoning 128

lentil 128, 129

lettuce 80, 106, 107

lime 72, 124, 140, 142

M

macadamia 33, 58, 59, 60, 61, 62, 65, 134

maple syrup 58, 186

marinade 117, 118, 119, 123

marjoram 152, 153

mayonnaise 98, 99

Mighty Cautious 17, 28, 29, 31, 33

Mighty Nice 17, 28, 29, 33

Mighty Poor 17, 28, 29, 33

milk 63, 65, 66, 67, 68, 69, 70, 71, 72, 73, 74, 75, 76, 84, 126, 157, 182, 190

mint 80, 82, 83, 94, 95, 118, 122, 124, 196

monounsaturated fat 33

mozzarella cheese 90, 126, 159, 169

mung beans 148

mushrooms 146

mustard 80, 117, 118, 119, 120, 121, 126, 127
  Dijon mustard 126

N

nacho chips 168

nutmeg 192, 194

Nutrasource Diagnostics, Inc 11

nuts 33, 63, 65

nut butter 55

O

oatmeal 186

oats 30, 52, 53, 84, 176, 180, 194

OCD 11, 13, 25

ODD 11

olive 33, 46, 68, 69, 71, 72, 73, 74, 75, 76, 77, 80, 84, 86, 88, 90, 92, 96, 100, 102, 104, 108, 110, 117, 118, 120, 122, 124, 132, 134, 136, 138, 140, 142, 144, 146, 148, 150, 152, 157, 159, 160, 167, 169, 176, 178, 180, 182, 192, 194

Omega 7, 13, 17, 20, 21, 22, 29, 30, 33, 37, 38

Omega-3 13

Omega-6 13

onion 104, 105, 108, 109, 146, 147, 148, 149, 150, 151, 152, 153

orange 46
  mandarin orange 124, 134

orange 36, 73, 74

orange extract 196

oregano 160

P

papper 100

paprika 163

parmesan cheese 92, 150

parsley 146

pasta sauce 86, 88

peaches 46, 63, 66, 67, 73, 74, 140, 142, 164, 184, 194

peanut 67

pear 81, 94, 95, 98, 99, 161, 164

peas 30, 48, 49, 80, 122, 134, 136, 138, 146, 148

pecans 192

pepper 30, 48, 49, 82, 83, 98, 99, 100, 101, 102, 103, 104, 105, 106, 107, 108, 109, 110, 111, 122, 124, 126, 132, 136, 138, 140, 142, 144, 146, 159

pharmaceutical
   Adderall 10
   Ritalin 10

pineapple 74, 102, 103, 140, 142, 165

pizza sauce 90, 160

plum 136, 137

potato 31, 88, 89, 90, 91, 92, 93, 104, 105, 110, 111, 178

protein 26, 29, 35

protein/carb combo 29

pumpkin pie spice 192

R

raspberries 68, 72, 184, 196

rice wine vinegar 79

ricotta cheese 92, 156

S

salmon 122, 123, 130, 131

salsa 168

salt 9, 58, 59, 60, 61, 84, 100, 102, 104, 106, 108, 110, 124, 126, 136, 138, 140, 142, 144, 146, 176, 180, 186, 192

saturated fat 33

seafood. *See* fish

Sears, Barry 7, 10, 34

shrimp 142, 143

soy sausage 158

spaghetti squash 150

SPECT 11

spinach 132, 133, 134, 135

sprouts 30, 134, 135, 149

squash 30, 31, 82, 83

steak 29, 114, 117, 118, 119, 122, 123

stevia 63, 66, 67, 68, 69, 70, 71, 72, 73, 74, 75, 76, 77, 157, 180

strawberries 50, 54, 56, 57, 58, 59, 60, 61, 62, 69, 77, 144, 169, 184, 190, 196

strawberry extract 196

string cheese 164

sugar 9, 17, 25, 26, 27, 31, 32, 34, 35, 36, 39

sweet potato 192

T

tamari 117, 118, 119, 120, 121, 148, 149

tangerine 94, 95

Threshold 13

thyme 152, 153

tofu 67, 74, 124, 148

tomato 80, 82, 83, 106, 107, 146, 150, 152
   tomato salsa 159

tomatoes 108

tuna 104, 105

turkey 28, 56, 57, 86, 87, 90, 91, 94, 95, 98, 99, 106, 107, 108, 109, 126, 150, 152, 166, 168

V

vanilla 58, 59, 60, 61, 66, 68, 69, 71, 75, 76, 77, 157, 176, 180, 182, 184, 186, 190, 192, 194

vegetables 30, 31

vegetarian 29

REMEMBER US EVERYTIME YOU EAT! WE'RE BEST FRIENDS - WE ALWAYS STAY TOGETHER!

Balance is the most important thing to remember!

First choose your protein. Always try to make it a mighty nice choice!

Choose your carbohydrate. Make sure it is balanced with your protein, or Omega-1 and Omega-3 will have trouble helping you stay healthy.

Choose a mighty nice fat. You don't want your protein and carb sliding around in a pile of grease! Be really careful of the trans fats!

Watch out for caffeine! That could be why you can't sit still in school or pay attention at home!

Remember the basic rules! If you need help just e-mail us: kids@kidsneedusnow.org. Have fun!